WILTSHIRE WATER MEADOWS

Cover Pictures:
(front) Hatches above Standlynch Mill on the River Avon (see pages 55 and 57)
(back) Wiltshire Horn: modern prizewinning ram (see page 99) photo by Noel Haring, reproduced from the breed society history (Thwaites)
Semi-diagrammatic sketch plan of floated water meadows at Lower Woodford on the River Avon (see page 32)

For Jennifer

A major hatch on a main carriage near Salisbury. This is being rebuilt in August 2005 as part of The Harnham Water Meadows Trust's restoration programme (classified by the Trust as Sluice 20). When complete the wooden frame will house two large wooden hatch boards (or paddles), raised and lowered by two steel rack and pinion devices to control the flow of water. Damage to the stone walls of the watercourse has been stabilised with cement infill. Part of the floor cleared of mud and rubble reveals stone blocks laid longitudinally across the carriage and secured laterally with iron cramps, sealed with lead to prevent the iron rusting and damaging the stone. They appear to have done this successfully for three centuries as the stone is judged to have come from the Hurdcott quarry some six miles west of Salisbury, geologically Upper Greensand, in the late seventeenth or early eighteenth century.

Wiltshire Water Meadows

understanding and conserving the remains of a
farming and engineering revolution

Michael Cowan

First published in the United Kingdom in 2005 by
The Hobnob Press, PO Box 1838, East Knoyle, Salisbury SP3 6FA

British Library Cataloguing in Publication Data
A catalogue record for this book is available from the British Library.

ISBN 0-946418-38-1

Typeset in 11/13.5 pt Scala
Typesetting and origination by John Chandler
Printed in Great Britain by Salisbury Printing Company Ltd, Salisbury

Contents

Colour plates between pages 72 and 73 deal with Rivers, Bridges, Meadows, Hatches, Structures, Access, Drowning, Aqueducts and Harnham . The captions follow the plates section. Measured drawings of structures are on pages 94, 97, 113, 114, 115.

Introduction

This work is about irrigation, its contribution to Wiltshire's agricultural economy in the past and the potential for its environmental usefulness now. Irrigation, watering in one way or another to improve a crop occurs in many parts of the world and in various different forms in this country. As a local historian I have focussed on what I know, the 'floated' bedwork systems of the chalk valleys in Wiltshire.

Interest was first aroused when a military career brought me to Salisbury in 1975, a Harnham home. and work first in the headquarters at Wilton and then the Ministry of Defence at Andover. The combination of a rather nine to five job at the latter and living beside the sadly neglected Harnham meadows provoked curiosity to know something about them and their watercourses. The local rector was kind enough to explain that the regular ridges were for the cows to stand and keep dry when the river flooded. Local history is full of myths and this sounded more than usually implausible. My first efforts brought me to Eric Kerridge who, in the mid twentieth century, researched and wrote extensively about seventeenth and eighteenth century agriculture.

His earliest relevant work was published in the *Wiltshire Archaeological and Natural History Magazine* (fondly known as *WAM*) in 1953. The first paragraph of 'The floating of the Wiltshire water meadows' is striking

> From the latter part of the seventeenth century to the latter part of the nineteenth the floated water-meadow was one of the greatest achievements of English agriculture and an integral part of the sheep-and-corn husbandry of the downlands of Wiltshire, Dorset, Berkshire and Hampshire. In Chalk Wiltshire in this period the overwhelming majority of the several and common meadows by the streamside were floated.

Half a century later a brisker comment on water meadows by Bruce Purvis (our Local Studies Librarian at Salisbury, in his 2003 work on the city) is that they were simply an 'economic power house'.

Discovering Kerridge and his later work prompted my own research, which merely recorded a number of systems. This was published as a 12 page monograph by the South Wiltshire Industrial Archaeology Society in 1982 while I was serving abroad – Zimbabwe, in happier times and also a place where irrigation was significant. This absence, a return to (the then) Humberside, a short return to work at Andover and retirement from the Army rather put meadows out of mind. A busy second career in the museum world and then for some years as General Secretary of the British Association for Local History kept them there. I felt that I had played a small part in actually recording a very few of the archaeological remnants in the hope of raising some awareness and interest.

By 2003, a certain amount of documentary research had been published in the wake of Kerridge but nothing similar to my original modest 'field walking' effort had appeared. This seemed a shame and my first task on retiring for the second time was to produce this book. Not in the best of health and rather less vigorous and agile than a quarter of a century ago there has been much less walking the ground and more observation from roads and bridges. There is a positive aspect to this limitation in that much of what I describe can be seen without getting too wet and muddy and I hope this will encourage others to observe in the same way; although getting wet and muddy can have its appeal. The great surprise on returning to the subject was to discover that historians and archaeologists had been joined by scientists with an interest in the characteristics of the chalk valleys. I hope that the possible modern environmental benefits of water meadows now becoming apparent are adequately reflected here.

My thanks of course are due to many people. Historian Dr Joe Bettey has made pre-publication drafts of his recent work available to me. Hydrologist Dr Hadrian Cook has been my soil science adviser. I have had help with the history and archaeology of the Harnham Meadows from Tim Tatton-Brown. Howard Jones, architect and field archaeolgist, has provided me with maps and measured drawings of structures; the latter are the first such, I think, to be published. As do most local historians in south Wiltshire I have reason to be grateful to the staff of Salisbury Local Studies Library for their patient ability to produce many of the early maps and obscure sources that I have needed. Dr John Chandler's unrivalled knowledge of Wiltshire history has been available to me and I am grateful for his many suggestions about sources. There are many more people who have answered questions and made suggestions.

Finally and most importantly I have to thank my family for their help and support over many years. For this recent work there has been a great deal of chauffeuring and typing. My two daughters and my son are now grown up but have continued to help and I hope that this work will be sufficient reward for enduring a lifetime of 'Daddy's meadows'.

Michael Cowan
8 May 2005

1
Meadows

HISTORY

Floated water meadows are the most easily seen but equally easily overlooked aspect of the agricultural story of much of Wiltshire and parts of the adjacent counties. They are generally the residual evidence of the sheep/corn system that provided much of the wealth of the county from the seventeenth to the nineteenth centuries. The sheep/corn system depended on maintaining very large flocks of sheep to graze on the downs and the meadows, and to be folded (secured in 'folds' or 'enclosures' of hurdles) on the arable fields by night. This manured the ground, restored fertility and maintained the corn harvest. Floating, or irrigating, the meadows improved their economic value by producing abundant grass early in the year when the downs became bare, thus enabling a farmer to keep more sheep and improve the corn crop.

   Our knowledge from contemporary documents about what actually happened is patchy but for the turn of each century there is useful published material. A start point concerning the sheep/corn system is a published summary about farming at Shrewton for some forty years from 1596;

> Judging from his inventories and notes, it was primarily in corn-growing that Wansborough was interested, though he sold wool in large quantities . . . the production of both was combined in the traditional sheep-and-corn husbandry of the Chalk country of Wiltshire . . . In Robert Wansborough, then, we see one of the capitalist farmers of the open fields and the sheep-and-corn regions . . . who loomed so large in the social history of the seventeenth century (Kerridge 1952/WAM 54)

The seventeenth century was one of development and during the eighteenth there was an almost universal application of the practice throughout the chalklands of Wessex. During the nineteenth century agriculture changed radically and floated water meadows lost their significance; few systems survived for long into the twentieth. At the beginning of the twenty-first century there is a revival of interest; a few working systems remain, the agricultural scientists have arrived and the environmentalists are recognising ecological value.

In 1653 Walter Blith published his *The English Improver Improved or the Survey of Husbandry Surveyed*. This has descriptions of various designs including what appear to be rudimentary bedwork systems. However, at least in Wiltshire, there is evidence of more mature work, that on the Pembroke lands for example. Later, in the 1660s Robert Seymer produced a report to the newly established Royal Society on the agriculture of the Dorset and Wiltshire chalklands, which focused substantially on the arable system and the need for large flocks. Evidence from this first hand survey and a wide range of documentary references has been gathered by Dr Joseph Bettey for the Wiltshire Record Society and distilled in thirty or so pages as the introduction to his edition of Wiltshire 17th century farm accounts (WRS;Bettey 2005).

Population increased dramatically in the seventeenth century. It is surmised to have been some two and a half million in 1558, at between four and five million in the reign of James 1, perhaps another half million by 1630 and a century later probably over seven million (Arnold-Baker 1996). These numbers drove a demand for more corn to feed the growing towns and to which the landowners of the south west chalklands tried to respond. They were constrained by the age old barrier of 'the hungry gap'. This was at the end of winter, when new grass had yet to appear whilst hay from the previous year had been exhausted. It limited the stock that could be kept and folded, thus preventing improvement to the corn crop.

Manorial records illustrate pressure to increase the arable acreage and the size of flocks, and arguments about exactly when lambs had to be counted as sheep. This was only nudging at the problem and the real solution was to irrigate the water meadows, increase the early grass and close the 'hungry gap'. The idea is said to have come to Rowland Vaughan in Herefordshire towards the end of the sixteenth century and become more widely known when he published *Water Workes* in 1610. There is an unsourced anecdote that the idea came to him when a tunneling mole created a leak from a mill leat (Delorme) but however it happened the limited initiative in Herefordshire was taken up by the Earls of

Pembroke on their estates in South Wiltshire and on the River Kennet. This was to float the flat valley bottoms of the chalk rivers, harnessing the flow, temperature and nutritional value of the water by complex control systems. The practicalities of floating (or constructing) and drowning (or operating) what are today sometimes classified as 'bedwork meadows' are explained below.

A century later in revolutionary and dangerous times the government was looking to food security and the adequacy of farming. A review with recommendations for improvements was published for many counties. That for Wiltshire was produced by Thomas Davis, Steward to Lord Bath at Longleat (described by one modern work as a 'civil servant'). Davis rode around the county, observed, consulted and produced his *General View of the Agriculture of Wiltshire drawn for the consideration of the Board of Agriculture and Internal Improvement.* The first edition was published in 1794. Some recommendations clearly did not please everyone, and after an intervening edition, that of 1813 tells us that differences are resolved.

Thomas Davis died in 1807 and the 1813 edition (used for this work) was prepared by his son, also Thomas. On the title page the son declares he does not seek the honour due to his father (*Patri debitum filius non petit honorem*). The work provides a full and clear view of how floated meadows were constructed and why, how they operated, and how they added value to the sheep/corn cycle. At the end of the eighteenth century the system had reached its apogee. What had been innovative in the seventeenth century was the established practice in the eighteenth. Davis captures the time and provides the definitive contemporary work.

There is no comparable formal material a century on again. However in the early 1930s AG Street, a farmer at Wilton, turned to writing and used what he knew about to produce lightly disguised fictional and other work that illustrates local farming well back into the nineteenth century. He provides, in effect, the negative evidence that tells us something has stopped. There is also locally published material dealing with sheep for the same period.

In 1999 Drs Hadrian Cook and Tom Williamson lecturers in respectively hydrology and landscape history edited *Water management in the English Landscape* which explores the science, history, management and conservation of water meadows. It reflects the new found interest of those concerned with the management of water and its importance to those in many fields such as historians, archaeologists, ecologists and environmentalists. Thus at the end of the twentieth century evidence of the earlier irrigation of the chalkland rivers took on a new significance.

WORKING

That floated (or bedwork) water meadows provide an important aspect of agricultural archaeology in south Wiltshire, as well as more widely in the south west, can readily be seen by glancing at the right sort of map. The Ordnance Survey 1:25,000 Explorer series clearly show the remnants of a significant irrigation system. The sheets covering the area north and south of Salisbury (130 and 157) show a network of water courses, standing out in blue, along the river valleys. Those shown are only the main elements of an intricate system, the fine detail of which is only to be seen on the larger scale maps. Even on them the details are liable to be incomplete, misleadingly titled and difficult to interpret. They are becoming increasingly hard to interpret as the visible remains on the ground are steadily destroyed by river maintenance and agricultural development, or just allowed to decay.

Chapter 2 describes and illustrates varying amounts of detail for several systems, including one still in reasonable working order. Most of what is described can be seen from roads or other rights of way. The general locations are shown in Figure 2.1 and a number of grid references are given. The diagrams are not generally to scale because much of the detail is enlarged for clarity. Guide distances are shown in some cases. There is little agreement about terminology but this work generally follows Davis.

The lucid work of Thomas Davis (and his son) is fundamental to understanding how floated meadows are constructed and how they served their purpose. The printed and published editions of their reports, in book form, are accessible in Local Studies and other specialist reference libraries but not easily and casually available. There is modern published work that describes the floating and drowning of meadows together with the consequential agricultural practices and animal husbandry. Most modern works cite or quote briefly from Davis but vary widely in effectiveness and there is no real substitute for going back to the original and definitive material. For that reason lengthy extracts are reproduced in Annex 2.

The elder Davis must have had a sense of humour and was not above trenchant criticism of practices he saw, riding about the county. He declares that it was impossible 'to give any intelligible description of the mode of making these meadows' and promptly attempts to do just that. He does add the rider that they need to be seen to be understood properly. This work seeks to help in that understanding.

The final edition of Davis's work, published in 1813, is a surprisingly modern looking hardback book with thirteen introductory and 258 main pages about A5 in size. There are only two illustrations, an engraving of Thomas Davis and another of 'A Wiltshire Ram' picturing the distinctive horned breed. The work distinguishes the contrasting 'chalk and cheese' characteristics of the county in separate parts. He allots 159 pages to the chalk, the 'south-east district', followed by 95 to the 'north-west district'. Within the first part relevant material for this work totals some thirty pages, from three of the sections.

Firstly, in those pages dealing with common fields he set out 'the custom of feeding the commonable lands, and the number of each stock each commoner . . . has a right to put on them '. The final pages of those reproduced explain why and how sheep are dealt with; the sheep stock, he says, 'is an object of the greatest importance. It may, indeed, be called the basis of Wiltshire Down husbandry'. More material on the Wiltshire Horn breed is in Chapter 5.

Between the topics, in those pages dealing with irrigation, he identifies the essential characteristics of a floated water meadow as a head of water on the river and a network of structured watercourses to create a flow down a shallow even sloping valley floor. This network consists of the main carriage from the river, with one or more sets of hatches, feeding a series of carriers along ridges, some with their own hatches and stops. These can be manipulated to create an even flow down the sides, or panes of each ridge and, via interlocking drains and tail drains, return the water to a lower point on the river. He deals with the theory of water meadows, their nature and properties, describes them and their management, and urges their advantages for sheep and hay.

Material from all parts of the extract combine to give a detailed picture of the annual cycle both for the irrigated systems and the sheep. In the autumn, he says, when the 'after grass' is eaten off quite bare (by cattle) the 'manager of the mead', or drowner, 'rights up the works' to make good the carriages and drains trodden by the cattle. Once one 'pitch of work' is ready it is put under water while the drowner prepares the next pitch. All this work should be done by Michaelmas (29 September). There is then intermittent watering with the ground as dry as possible in between to encourage the growth and quality of the grass.

For the sheep he says that rams are put to the ewes about mid September. Then 'As soon as the lambs are able to travel with the ewes (perhaps about the middle of March), the flock is put into the water meadows'. These have to be dry and on account of the 'quickness' of the grass the flock does not go on to it with empty bellies or before the dew has gone. They feed 'from ten or eleven in the morning, to four or five in the evening, when the sheep are driven to the fold...generally on the barley-fallow' (ploughed but not yet sown). While a flock is on the meadows, Davis goes on, 'The grass is daily hurdled out in portions, according to the number of sheep, to prevent their trampling it down; but a few spaces are left in the hurdles for the lambs to get through, and feed forward in the fresh grass. These spaces were also known as 'lamb creeps' defined (D and G 1893) as 'a hole in the hurdles to enable the lambs to get out'.

One acre of good grass was deemed sufficient for 500 couples (comprising a ewe and her lamb): the great object was to make the water-meadow grass last till the barley sowing was finished. When this first crop of grass was finished the water was 'immediately thrown over the meadows and they are then made perfectly dry, and laid up for hay'. This crop could be taken, exceptionally, after five weeks but more usually six, and occasionally eight. If hay was scarce a second crop might be attempted but generally the later grass was more suitable to be grazed by cattle which could remain until the drowner began preparing for the winter watering.

There are no contemporary illustrations or diagrams in Davis, nor apparently elsewhere. Modern work of this nature exists, particularly the diagrams in Chapter 2. There are also a number of modern attempts to illustrate a notional system in diagrammatic form. One such, in a contribution (Bettey 1978), part of *A guide to the Industrial Archaeology of Wiltshire* (ed Corfield) is reproduced here in Figure 1.1. This diagram has been widely reproduced and provides a schematic guide, not unlike the classic map of the London Underground. However, and with due deference to the definitive work of Dr Bettey, in one particular it can be improved. It is commonly found that a main carriage or mill leat will leave the river by going straight on, an obviously man made, sometimes embanked, structure. In contrast the river bends into its natural curve, dropping sideways over a weir in the process. This point is more clearly shown in two otherwise quite different ways of attempting to show how a system worked, both included in the figure (Boswell 1779; Clark 2004). The inclusion of water meadows in the 1978 work is also an early, and possibly the first, classification of an agricultural process as 'industrial archaeology', although a separate classification as 'agricultural archaeology' is perhaps to be preferred. There are also photographs of some systems that survived into the twentieth century, aerial shots being particularly useful. One such, taken in 1982, of part of a system at Homington,

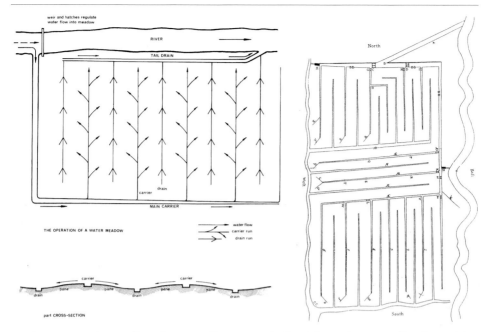

1.1 *Attempts to show a floated system diagrammatically: (above) Bettey 1978; (above right) Boswell 1779; (below) Clark 2004. The last probably gives the best impression, but what would elsewhere be called hatches are shown here as 'stops' with drop boards, apparently characteristic of systems on the River Wey in Hampshire. See also the semi-diagrammatic representation of a real system in Figure 2.5.*

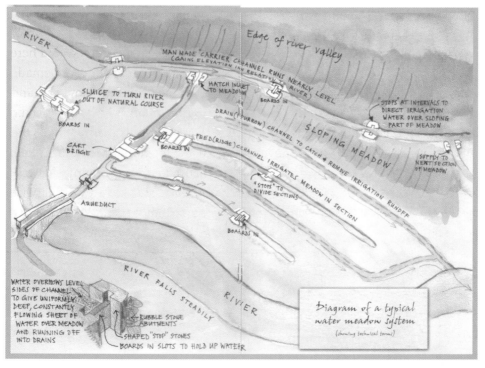

1.2 *Aerial view of part of Homington meadows on the River Ebble south of Salisbury. North is to the top of the picture, the river flows from left to right along the foot, and Homington Bridge, formerly carrying an important road, is at bottom right. (© Wiltshire County Council)*

below Coombe Bissett on the River Ebble (© Wiltshire County Council, Libraries and Heritage) is shown here as Figure 1.2. A useful source is the vast coloured Millennium aerial photograph of the Salisbury aerial displayed in Salisbury Library.

ENVIRONMENT

Introduction
To get the best out of bedwork floated water meadow ('ingredients for optimal meadow productivity' as a scientist puts it) several factors have been identified (Cook and Williamson 1999; Cook 2003).

- natural regulation of the hydrological system through chalk aquifers
- appropriate valley gradients
- a strong culture of water management in the region
- alluvial soils and underlying gravel to suit bedwork construction and drainage
- favourable hydrochemical conditions in chalk waters as a buffer against acidity
- thermal conditions of chalk water that warm the soil in winter and early spring
- a fine clay and silt component in the rivers to bring on nutrients

Pioneers of the seventeenth century and the observers, such as Thomas Davis at the end of the eighteenth, knew how to construct the irrigation systems they called 'floated water meadows'. Practically, they knew how to operate them to best advantage and what worked. In the long extracts from the 1794/1813 work Davis writes 'The idea of taking the water off the land, and bringing it on again at will, is the suggestion of art; and the knowledge of the proper time of doing this, is the result of observation'. They were aware of the significance of the geology, water and of temperature. What they did not know, as we do now, is why it all worked.

Four major factors came together to create the agricultural success story of the floated meadows. The geology of the Wessex chalkland was favourable and the water was suitable. The topography, the natural features of the area, particularly the alluvial soils of the floodplain, lent itself to the development. And finally it was down to landuse: the pattern of occupancy and how landowners and farmers applied the natural advantages to their agricultural practice.

Recent agricultural scientific work on which much of this section is based (Cook 2003) has suggested that bedwork water meadows, the zenith of a technology, were apparently and with varying degrees of success widespread across Europe at sites where they were favoured by the land form, the soil, the climate and the water. 'Strong environmental factors central to effective water meadow construction . . . optimized the benefits of floating in the 'core area' of Wessex in addition to the economic and agronomic factors that favoured the development'.

Geology

The geology of the relevant parts of Wessex is chalk downland (paradoxically the high ground) divided by river valleys with, generally speaking, alluvial deposits over gravel. The chalk is an unusually pure soft limestone, largely calcium carbonate, up to some 500 metres in thickness in south Wiltshire and the surrounding areas. Chalk is generally about 40% porosity, the tiny pores being less than 0.001 millimetres in diameter. Water is transmitted by both vertical and horizontal orthogonal fissures, typically between 0.05 and 5 millimetres wide and between 0.1 and 0.2 metres apart. The chalk constitutes an 'aquifer' (water bearer), absorbing rainfall and discharging it at springs and seepage into rivers throughout the year. (Aquifers are not, as they are sometimes described, 'sponges' or 'reservoirs' as those terms are commonly understood). The porous chalk contains water at, typically, 10 or 11 degrees centigrade and tends to reach the meadows above 5.5 degrees, the temperature that triggers the growth of temperate zone grass, typical of the floodplains of Britain (Cook 2003).

Along the valleys the meadows are, in scientific terms, analogous with hydroponic propagation. The surface layer of the water is constantly dissolving oxygen from the air, avoiding anoxic or 'reducing' conditions in the soil that are detrimental to most plants, as is substantial loss of nitrogen to the atmosphere. In earlier, colder centuries ('Little Ice Age' approx 1500 to 1850 in Britain) the function of irrigation to warm the soil and protect early growth from frost was significant. The gravel bed below the alluvial soil provided a sound base for bedwork construction and can assist drainage, particularly if set in a 'sandy matrix'. A loam based subsurface was less satisfactory and accounts for the need to 'break up' the ground often recorded during the initial work.

Topography

The significant topographic features of the Wessex chalk country are the downland and the river valleys. Figure 1.3 shows diagrammatically a typical plan and profile. The relatively narrow flat valley floor tends to be flanked by slightly

VALLEY PROFILE

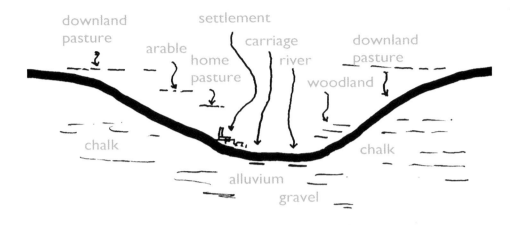

VALLEY PLAN

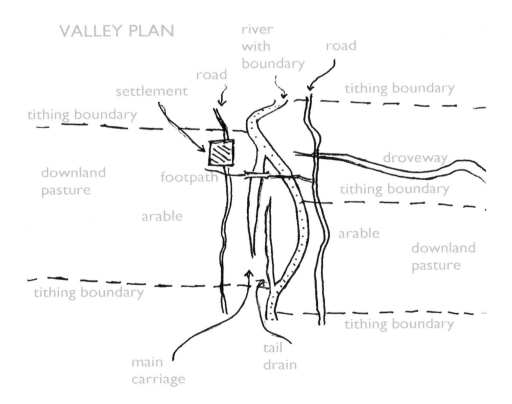

1.3 *Top: Notional but typical valley profile. Bottom: Notional plan of valley topography with floated systems and tithings.*

higher terraces where villages are situated above flood level. The terraces tend also to carry the roads or tracks which almost always follow the course of the valley. Periodically, at right angles, are the droveways to move flocks to and from the downs and meadows. The ground then rises, sometimes with a steep convex slope, sometimes more softly, to the top of the downs. The rivers drop quite gently but have sufficient force to power mills and to provide the many heads of water needed by the almost continuous meadow systems. The (Hampshire) Avon rises in central Wiltshire near Pewsey and flows generally due south to the coast at Christchurch in Hampshire (now Dorset), a point to point distance of some forty five miles and possibly some sixty miles of river (maybe 100 kilometres).

At Pewsey the valley floor is at around 115 metres above sea level, the downs on either side rise to over 200m. Twenty-four kilometres or so downstream, at Amesbury, the valley floor is at 70m, and the downs of Salisbury Plain generally reaching 100m to 200metres in elevation. By the time the river reaches Britford, just below Salisbury, the valley floor is 43m, the high ground rising on each side to some 80-100m. The fall of the floodplain between Amesbury and Britford has been calculated as 1 metre in 800. Further downstream between Downton and Ringwood this reduces to 1:1,200. The River Avon itself is typical in that it follows a sinuous course within its valley, curving from side to side, creating the long shallow bends that suit the floated systems.

Landuse

'Landuse' is a modern term, beloved of planners, but clear in its meaning and has economic overtones. It is first identified by the OED in 1935. Anachronistic or not it is a useful term to describe the environment created by the pattern of land occupancy and the use to which it was put. There is a pattern of villages strung at intervals along the Wessex valleys with territorial boundaries of great antiquity. Saxon boundary charters provide evidence of the rectangular 'tithings'. One of many meanings for this is an administrative area supporting ten households which seems a better description than a Wiltshire dialect meaning of ten sheaves. These survived as parishes long enough to be surveyed in the nineteenth century and can still to some extent be detected in modern administrative boundaries. Characteristically the short sides of the rectangle (Figure 1.3) are along the river and the ridge at the top of the downs; the long boundaries, at right angles to the river are shared with the villages on each side.

1.4 No-one in the past seems to have illustrated the valleys and downs other than as incidental to Salisbury Cathedral. Here, in 1827, John Britton's viewpoint was on Harnham Hill above Old Blandford Road near the modern television mast. The confluence of the rivers Nadder and Avon is obscured by trees. In the distance are Bemerton Heath to the left (west) and Bishopdown to the east.

The scene appears in fictional form in *Strawberry Roan* (Street 1932). The roan calf of the title is one of several being driven from market (in a thinly disguised Salisbury) in 1928.

> Their road, an old Ox Drove, led them to the top of the Wiltshire downs, along whose ridge they travelled for the major part of the journey . . . and from which could be seen . . . the valley beneath . . . the vivid lush green carpet of the water meadows through which ran the river like a wandering bright silver thread . . . Beyond were the different colours of the crops sloping up to the opposite ridge of downs.

The calves turn off the Drove 'down a rutted chalk road leading through Springhead Farm', their new home. Later in the work the young tenant farmer, Christopher Lowe (who eventually fails through a combination of bad farming luck and living beyond his means) takes an early morning ride around his farm. After seeing the shepherds at work in the sheepfold he rides up hill to where 'the carters were busy dressing down the fallow'. From this vantage point he obtained a beautiful bird's eye view of the farmhouse and buildings with the valley beyond. There was a dairy herd in the big water meadow . . . calves in the home pasture . . . Peeps of grey stone . . . between the gaps in the trees around the steading, and far across the valley on the other slope up from the river to the downs was the glorious patchwork of the different cropped fields belonging to his neighbour.

In the nursery rhyme (Opie 1961), Little Boy Blue is urged to

> come blow up your horn
> the sheep are in the meadow
> the cows in the corn

Self evidently the cows are in the wrong place but why the sheep? In normal farming circumstances it was pasture that was grazed by stock, thus sheep would be on the 'downland pasture', and the richer meadows reserved for the hay crop, stock excluded. Irrigating the water meadows to provide sheep with their early bite (and, by this time, used for cattle) must have been confusing to the poor boy.

Very sensibly every such community thus had its share of downland, arable, meadow and river (Chandler 1983; 1987). The way in which this mix of

1.5 View from the medieval Old Sarum Castle in March 2005 looking slightly north of west to Camp Down some two kilometres away; the outline of the first, eleventh century, Salisbury Cathedral is in the foreground.

characteristics was used no doubt changed over many centuries. During the seventeenth, eighteenth and nineteenth however there is abundant evidence of almost total absorption with using the arable to produce corn with the aid of 'walking fertiliser' provided by sheep. Downs and meadows supported the stock; the river provided the water and motive power to irrigate and improve the meadows.

There is some evidence of the physical appearance of early floated meadows. Blith offers descriptions of the first systems in 1657 but Davis in 1794 and 1813 has probably left the fullest description. He also, as we have noted, describes flocks as being folded on the commonable water meadows - 'the grass is daily hurdled out in portions... a few spaces are left in the hurdles for the lambs to get through, and feed forward in the fresh grass'. The term 'lamb's creep' is recognised in the Dartnell and Goddard dictionary of Wiltshire dialect as 'a hole in the hurdles for the lambs to get out of the fold'. All this suggests that the valley bottom was fairly bare of anything but the all important grass and the devices and channels that provided its irrigation.

This must have changed with Inclosure (or in more common modern usage - Enclosure). Acts of Parliament averaged 47 a year in the twenty years from 1765. In 1802 there were 119; by 1845, nationally, nearly 4000 separate acts were in existence. The massive legal and tenurial changes involved were matched by the changed face of much of the landscape and the Wessex chalkland was no exception. New holders were habitually required to plant quickset hedges as a condition of taking up their holdings but this may not have been appropriate on irrigated meadows.

The Harnham meadows (see Chapter 4) were enclosed in 1787. The contemporary map shows the boundaries of the various 'mead' holdings delineated by pollarded willows (Figure 1.6). Whether this practice was widespread is unclear but makes eminent sense. There were certainly withy beds where willow was cropped to provide the hurdles needed for the sheepfolds and other farming needs, for example the teeth of hay rakes. Today willows in full growth are to be seen along the watercourses, pollards more rarely. There are hedges and sometimes long disused and neglected pieces of meadow become woodland. At Harnham the managing Trust have actually planted variegated copses as part of their environmental conservation management programme. Another landowner some years ago was planting willows destined to become cricket bats.

1.6 Part of the 1787 map accompanying the West Harnham inclosure award. The two arms of the River Nadder at the top encompass the meadows now owned and managed by the Harnham Water Meadows Trust (see Chapter 4). This copy is reproduced by courtesy of Tim Tatton Brown, who added the shading to show different ownership and occupancy.

REGENERATION

The title of the lecture reproduced as Annex 3 uses the word 'decline' and implies an end, floated water meadows and the sheep corn cycle consigned to historians and archaeologists. That was then; now their interest remains important but others have arrived, notably scientists and environmentalists, to re-ignite interest and activity. One such scientific view is that

> control of water has played a key, and much neglected, role in the development of agriculture in England. More importantly the surviving remains of past management systems, and their associated habitats, form a vital element in the countryside: an understanding of their history is essential for all custodians of the natural, as well as the archaelogical, heritage. Water management systems represent one fascinating example of the complex and dynamic relationship between human societies and the natural world (Cook and Williamson 1999).

Most floated water meadows today are good examples of an increasingly rare managed wetland habitat, unimproved by modern agriculture. They support a wide variety of native grasses, herbaceous plants and a rich range of trees and shrubs. The damp soft substrata encourage bird life. Butterflies and other invertebrates are common. Designations as Sites of Special Scientific Interest (SSSI) or Areas of Outstanding Natural Beauty (AONB) are frequent. The Department for Environment, Food and Rural Affairs (DEFRA), the Environment Agency (EA), English Nature (EN), and some local authorities are all official bodies that provide advice, support and, less often, money for those who today try to manage the agricultural archaeological heritage of the Wessex chalkland water meadows. One has to feel that, although he might have a problem with the alaphabet soup, Thomas Davis would approve.

In Dorset ' a partnership for the conservation and enjoyment of Purbeck' has been set up, and for Maiden Newton Water Meadow, on the River Frome, Dorset County Council in the guise of

> Dorset Countryside has been working with the landowner to restore this small water-meadow. It is our intention to rebuild the sluices and dig out the channels and drains so that we can work this system once more. If you would like to visit this beautiful area, please use . . . permissive path . . . to the River Frome and the water-meadow. (Elliott, undated leaflet)

This coloured leaflet, produced before 1997 (a separately documented Countryside Stewardship Scheme has a ten year currency from 1999), describes the historical purpose of floating, has an accurate description and diagram of the process and outlines modern plans to restore appropiate vegetation by grazing. But the real stress is on plants and insects, 'creepy crawlies' that will emerge as colourful dragonflies and damselflies. Visitors are encouraged to use the dipping platform to observe fish and small water insects. There is no map but to help identification there is a key illustrating no less than thirty three specimens, from a conical pond snail to a China Mark Moth caterpillar.

Hampshire claims to have 'nearly half of all water meadows found in England which makes them of national significance'. The priority here seems somewhat different. One published document contains this highlighted paragraph

> It is, however, important to recognize the intrinsic historic and archaeological interest of these structures if water meadows are not to become **merely** wetland sites of ecological value [author's added emphasis] which ignore their historic agricultural function and archaeological and landscape value (Hampshire County Council, undated but after 2002)

This work is *The conservation of water meadows* (Clark 2004), a ten page booklet, publicizing the outcome of a 1999 desk-based survey by the Oxford Archaeological Unit to compare 1996 aerial photographs with the 1874 Ordnance Survey. No fewer than 322 separate blocks were identified, nearly continuous along the valleys of the rivers Avon, Test, Itchen, Meon and their tributaries, and also to be found on the Wey, Lodden and Wallington. It concluded that, of the original meadows, 4% could be classified as 'well preserved' and 40% had been destroyed; between 1970 and 1996 over a third had deteriorated.

There may be other efforts, but this appears to be a groundbreaking work. Well illustrated, see Figure 1.7, it is concerned only with structures and suggests that

> The level of intervention will vary from doing nothing to full restoration, but ... management which promotes awareness of the existence of structures, their location and type and measures to prevent deterioration is an appropriate approach

Its sections deal with vegetation, masonry, timber, metalwork, timber and site observation followed by twenty two illustrated examples of best practice.

simple inscription or discrete non-corrosive plaque would be appropriate.

Salvaged timber and ironwork used in conjunction with new timber. Existing brickwork repaired and reinstated.

Smaller sluice board with original metal fixing mechanism. Boards raised and lowered manually without mechanised assistance.

Cast iron mechanism rescued and salvaged for storage/re-use. It is important to record the original location of these structures.

Brick aqueduct which has become overgrown. Careful cutting back of vegetation required and consolidation of the masonry.

New sluice boards in position. Some brick repair required to sides of channel at lower levels.

A new concrete/brick structure in this restored water meadow system retains the important tree.

Rebuilt structure using salvaged bricks and new metal sluice boards.

Clearly, the management of ditches and channels is an integral part of the water meadow system. **The Environment Agency has produced an advisory leaflet on Ditch Management.** Channels should not be cleared to more than their original dimension (depth and width).

1.7 Conservation of characteristic meadow structures: extract from an advisory booklet published by Hampshire County Council (Clark 2004).

For example, the shallow arched bridge

> needs some consolidation . . . loose bricks carefully retained . . . lime mortar used to repoint areas where water can be trapped . . . the moss, lichen and grass on the brickwork can be left

A matching, very unrestored, example photographed in Wiltshire in 2004 is shown as Figure 3.5d. The centrefold of the booklet is a boldly drawn three dimensional diagram of a system, also reproduced (Figure 1.1). A particular point of value is the depiction of an aqueduct across the river, taking water from one system to that on the opposite bank. (The former existence of these can be identified in Wiltshire but few, if any, seem to have survived.)

This conservation publication was preceded by a glossy ten page document *Water Meadows in Hampshire* (Hampshire County Council 2002) arising from the survey. To show diagrammatically how a system works it adopts a more conservative approach with '*An idealized plan of bed work system. Boswell 1779*'. reproduced from their version in Figure 1.1). Both these diagrams correctly make the distinction that the river turns into its curve and the straight leat or carriage tends to go straight on. The text describes and explains. It identifies water meadows as a defining component of the

1.8 A Wiltshire 'bog body'? Location map of the archaeological site on the Avon at Lake in the Woodford valley; the water meadow system, centre, is identified by the arrowed burial site (reproduced from WANHM 96, 2003, 8)

distinctive valley landscapes and declares their care to be part of the stewardship
of 'the sense of place that is Hampshire'. The actual four page policy document is
loose in a back cover pocket. The assertion stands to be corrected but this seems to
be the first of its kind. Whether so or not it is a major step in the continuing story
of chalkland irrigation and is reproduced in facsimile as Annex 4.

Back in Wiltshire there is perhaps less policy but certainly some action.
The Harnham Water Meadows Trust restoration programme has been going on
since 1989 and is covered extensively later in this work. Another possibly
memorable 'first' arises from 'A Wiltshire 'Bog Body' ?: Discussion of a Fifth/
Sixth Century AD Burial in the Woodford Valley' (McKinley 2003 in *WANHM*
96). This reports a watching brief by Wessex Archaeology in 1996 during the
construction of an amenity lake on the Avon at Wilsford-cum-Lake between
Amesbury and Salisbury. This revealed the body of the title, a matter of
considerable archaeological significance in this area of the 'Stonehenge Environs'.

However, of importance to this work, the initial field survey recorded
with archaeological precision

> A number of linear earthworks pertaining to the water meadow system were
> recorded comprising two carriages (east and west), one tail drain and a length of
> spillway . . . and 23 drains . . .

and goes on with measurement and interpretation. Part of the site location map
is shown in Chapter 3. The report concludes that the

> accidental discovery of this burial resulted from a rare intervention into the flood
> plain alluvium of the Woodford valley. These deposits have rarely been subject to
> archaeological investigation . . . prior disturbance is likely to have limited to the
> insertion of water-meadow systems in the 17th and 18th centuries where isolated
> deposits of this type, with no associated earth works or artifacts to attract attention,
> are likely to have passed un-noticed or have been ignored. There is high potential for
> further archaeologically significant deposits along the Woodford valley bottom . . .

The last few paragraphs have noted several different approaches to
recording and conserving floated systems, all of which have their place

- the practical - just get on with it, walk the ground, draw, photograph, dig out the
  channels, find the structures and restore or at least stabilize them
- the expensive – commission an aerial survey and a related map study of a whole
  area to inform more localized decisions
- the accidental – capitalize on someone else's archaeological investigation

A conference hosted by the Friends of the Harnham Water Meadows Trust and organized by the Department of Agricultural Sciences at Imperial College, University of London was held in Salisbury on 26-27 March 2004. Called *Towards a New Treatise on Watering, the science history, management, and conservation of the Water Meadows* – its orotund title was in the fine tradition of its predecessor studies of earlier centuries. The speakers included a landscape historian, hydrologist, agricultural academic, local historian, local government conservation officer, archaeologist and an adviser to DEFRA. The 'treatise' is to be published (Cook and Williamson 2005), including a chapter by Dr Kathy Stearne – the adviser to DEFRA – titled, 'Management of water meadows: four hundred years of intensive integrated agriculture', and explaining their continuing importance. With this interdisciplinary interest the future of these odd but rather special landscapes begins to look brighter than it did in 1982 when the earlier version of this work appeared.

The final paragraph of this introductory chapter might be headed 'Stop Press'. At a very late stage a leaflet appeared from English Heritage (EH 2005) announcing, in summary, some previously trailed changes to the statutory listing system. For buildings the changes were to be from April 2005 but, for this work, the important part is headed 'What Next?', indicating the intention of

> integrating the currently separate systems of listing buildings, scheduled monuments and archaeological sites and registering historic parks, gardens and battlefields into a unified heritage protection system

In particular the unified system would include the 'Provision of statutory management agreements for complex historic assets'. It is to be hoped that floated systems could benefit from qualifying for inclusion in this category. However primary legislation is likely to be needed and a national range of pilot projects are planned before it is drafted. One of the 15 projects is 'Water Meadows, Hampshire. A historic irrigation system on the banks of the River Itchen at Eastleigh'. Not exactly on the home territory of this book, but a hopeful step in the right direction.

2
Systems

INTRODUCTION

NOTE that most of the material in this Chapter should be read in conjunction with an Ordnance Survey map of the area, preferably 1:25000 (4 centimetres to one kilometre or two and half inches to one mile). The 1997 Explorer series is recommended, Sheet 157 for Ramsbury, 130 for the remaining examples. References to left and right of a watercourse are to be read as facing down stream.

The six illustrations of irrigated water meadows that follow are all of floated bedwork systems on Wiltshire rivers. One is on the River Kennet, one on the Wylye, two are on the upper Avon (above Salisbury) and one at the confluence of the Nadder and Avon. The sixth description, on the lower Avon (Salisbury to Downton) actually embraces a further seven systems.

The core material of Woodford (Avon) and Harnham (Nadder/Avon) together with lesser pieces on detail at Standlynch/Charlton and Downton are reproduced virtually unchanged from their original publication (Cowan 1982a). The Wishford (Wylye) piece is also repeated nearly unchanged from its publication in the *Hatcher Review* (Cowan 1982b). All these are demonstrated diagrammatically with textual explanation. The remaining three are new and intended to show aspects of investigation - the 'detective work' needed to interpret individual systems. The Ramsbury example is based on an Ordnance Survey map surveyed in 1885; for the lower Avon old and up to date Ordnance Survey material is used. The relatively tiny systems on the headwater of the Avon at Pewsey are based only on fieldwork, included to contrast with the relatively massive works on the

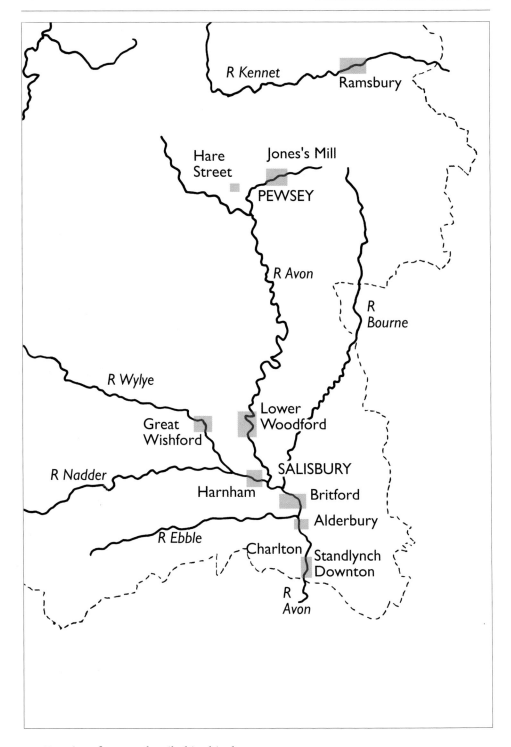

2.1 Location of systems described in this chapter.

lower reaches and to highlight the almost total extent of floated irrigation on the Avon, 'stretched to the limits of the valley', as on all the chalkland rivers. These locations are shown in Figure 2.1.

RAMSBURY

This first example of a floated water meadow is on the River Kennet, some seven miles east and downstream from Marlborough. It runs for a half mile or so from just below the park of Ramsbury Manor to the edge (the settlement boundary) of Ramsbury. The first Earl of Pembroke, based at Wilton House near Salisbury, had introduced floated bedwork meadows on the River Wylye in south Wilshire from about the 1620s. He is also recorded as floating a meadow on his Ramsbury estate at much the same time. It is not known if it was this stretch of the river but it can probably be dated generally to the seventeenth century.

The illustration for Ramsbury (Figure 2.2) is from an early Ordnance Survey map (Wiltshire 1:2500 Sheet 29.8) surveyed in 1885, revised 1899 and published 1900. The lack of irrigation detail is not a likely result of indifferent

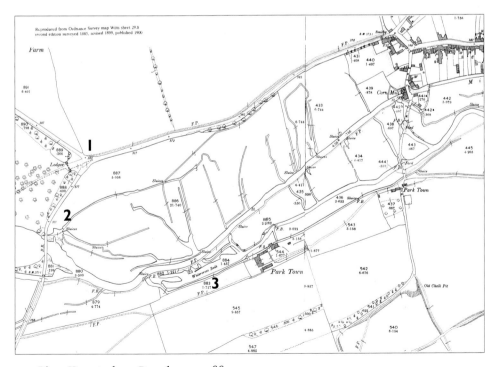

2.2 River Kennet above Ramsbury, c. 1885

surveying but of long disuse. There was a Second World War airfield on the nearby downs and aerial photographs of it in the late 1940s survive. Many show this part of the river and have been examined in the hope that a 'crop mark' type of detail might emerge - without success. However this is the sort of basic evidence that is often found. It has to be supplemented by work on the ground and with modern maps. Flashes of intuition help.

For research purposes it is useful to colour a photocopy of a black and white map, clearly to distinguish roads, paths and bridges from watercourses. However the example here is shown as it could be looked at in a Local Studies Library with nothing added or left out. Some of the printed numbers indicating land division (lots) and areas (in acres) are used as markers. The first thing to note is the road at the top coming, on the left, from Marlborough past a Ramsbury Manor lodge gate (382, **Point 1**) to Ramsbury on the right. At the edge of the village Mill Lane runs southwards across two fords with foot bridges (443.467) to Park Town. There is then a footpath, below all the watercourses, from right to bottom left where it meets the road bridging, first the tail drain from an upstream pitch, then the river, to rejoin the main road by the lodge gate. The modern Ordnance Survey 1:25000 Explorer sheet 157 will confirm that perambulation of this rectangular route can be made on public rights of way.

Turning to the watercourses the River Kennet comes in from upstream (at bottom left) widened into an ornamental lake in Ramsbury Manor Park and narrowing at the bridge. This 'houses' the hatches controlling a drop to enable the pitch below to be drowned. The system is fed initially by a conduit of some sort from the lake, beneath the road into a curiously shaped reservoir (below 371, **Point 2**) with four outlets. That to the south is the spillway to take surplus water back to the river. The other three (marked 'Sluices') supply the whole system.

The area of the reservoir and its outlets was grossly overgrown in about 1990 when the author surveyed the system, unwisely stepping on to a mat of tangled undergrowth and straight down into four feet of stagnant water. Fieldwork is not always comfortable but from the safety of the road more recently the scene appeared unchanged. The only hatch just visible, in ruins, is the one watering the main carriage along the top of the system roughly parallel to the road. There are some distinct oddities in what was surveyed arising no doubt from the natural distortions of long disuse, but the main thrust is clear.

Carriers and drains are at right angles to the main carriage and deliver water back towards what seems instinctively to be the river, passing under it to water the far side and then flow via the main tail drain off to the right to feed the next system downstream. This seems to make sense. Most of the stonework of the portals to what are presumably inverse syphons was there at the time of the c1990 survey and one of two seemed still to operate as a natural part of land drainage.

However a reconstruction map of Ramsbury in 1828 (Figure 2.3 from VCH 12) suggests something different. Ramsbury Manor lake is 'hatched' (different use of the word) and the river then flows downstream in a bow past Park Town. It follows exactly the line of the lower watercourse on the 1885 survey and bifurcates to cross Mill Lane, the left hand stream as a mill leat.

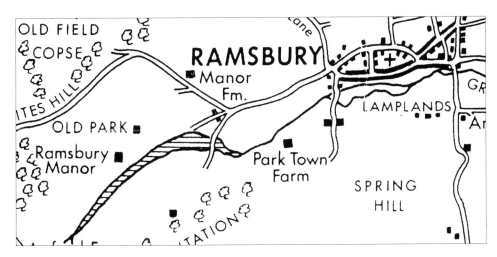

2.3 *The Ramsbury area c. 1828 as reconstructed by the VCH.*

What appears to have happened is that at some time in the mid-nineteenth century the mill leat was reconstructed as the long straight watercourse (which at a quick glance looks like the river) crossing the existing floated system. If water was not to be wasted it had to be passed underneath. Modern maps appear to confirm this. The Explorer Sheet 157 shows clearly that the wider upper watercourse, downstream of the mill, diminishes to a tail drain and that the lower, apparently lesser, one is clearly the river. Just to complicate matters one of the several watercress beds introduced in the Ramsbury area in the later nineteenth century was superimposed on part of the floated work between the two watercourses (884, **Point 3**); this one before, at latest, the 1899 revised survey.

It is not unusual to find systems changed over time and it is unwise to take things as they immediately appear without some reflection. And on the whole, rivers meander and manmade watercourses are usually straight (ish).

PEWSEY

This second example deals with two long disused sites on one of the two headwaters of the Hampshire Avon in central Wiltshire. This, eastern, arm rises to the north-east of Pewsey. The modern OS map shows some of the usual skeletal pattern of watercourses both above and below the town and the two specific sites are included to show that floating took place even on the relatively tiny amounts of meadow available in the steep and narrow valleys of the upper reaches of the chalk rivers.

Jones's Mill

The approach to this site is somewhat tentative. When the Wiltshire Wildlife Trust acquired the area as the Vera Jeans Nature Reserve, the author was invited to visit, in about 1986, to help identify the remains of any floated system. Nearly two decades on and rather less mobile, this recollection prompted a necessarily limited visit to the steep and wet site early in 2004. The description below stems from this visit and the illustration (Figure 2.4) is the Trust's map designed for all visitors and not particularly suited to studying the irrigation pattern. Coinciding with this visit was the publication of a very thorough study of the whole reserve (Heath *et al*, 2004) This deals substantially with habitat, but also maps the watercourses further upstream than has been attempted here. There is a convincing suggestion that there was a 'catchwork' system on the steep valley sides, a variant of the 'bedwork' layout on the flat valley floor considered throughout this work.

The site, some six or seven hundred metres upstream from Pewsey, is apparently so named because of a mediaeval reference but there is no mill now. The width of the infant Avon at this point is barely two metres (or perhaps a few feet) when flowing strongly early in the year. It waters a flat valley bottom of no more than a hundred metres. There is no public right of way but permissive paths provide access and facilitate crossing the marshy valley with wooden walkways. Entrance to the reserve (with limited parking space) is where the railway cutting is bridged at GR 170610. It is also possible to enter the reserve from the towpath of the Kennet and Avon Canal. The valley carries the canal on its 130 metre contour to the north and the railway to the south. From the railway bridge (at 134m) the line of the canal can be established by sight of Pains Bridge some five hundred metres to the north west. Visible between these two points are the tops of trees on the lower steep valley sides. The river and its narrow valley bottom (some twenty metres lower) cannot be seen but can be reached on foot by using the reserve paths and walkways.

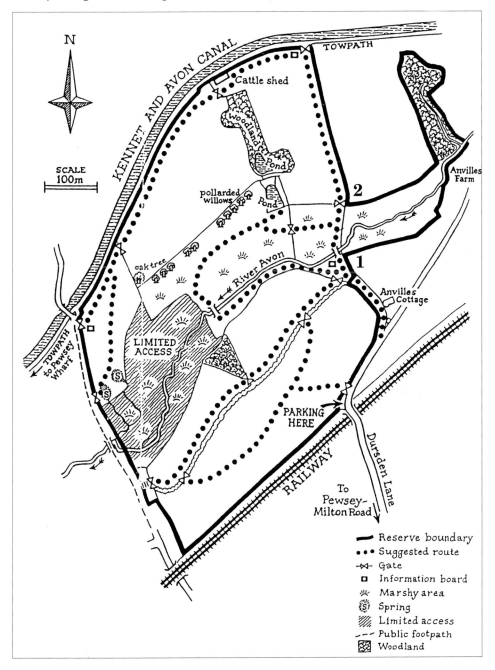

2.4 *Jones's Mill reserve on the River Avon at Pewsey*

On the ground there are occasional faint traces of the usual ridge and furrow layout and a few pieces of brickwork and timber providing some archaeological remnants to indicate former irrigation. Some of this can be determined from the rebuilt two arch brick footbridge shown in Figure 2.4 at Point 1 (GR 169613). The tiny river is close to the steep left side of the valley but it is at least conceivable that there were carriers on some parts of the very narrrow intervening flat strip. There are certainly situations on larger systems much further downstream where tiny pockets of land, often on the 'wrong' side of the river, have been floated.

However on the right bank the marshy valley bottom has been irrigated in the distant past. It is some eighty metres wide and can be crossed by the wooden walk way to the plank bridge at the gate and the point from which the ground starts to rise. The ditch bridged here will have been a main carrier from further upstream shown in Figure 2.4 as Point 2, turning diagonally back on itself after a hundred metres or so and flowing 'upstream' into the river just below the brick bridge. In the past this flow is more likely to have been from the river into a main carriage for the next pitch. Precisely how everything fitted together is lost.

The alignment illustrated is based on the Wildlife Trust's information boards as the marshy ground does not invite closer investigation. It is how the water does actually drain now and is a useful illustration of how long disuse can short circuit carriers to drains and the structure of a system becomes irretrievably confused. These meadows are said to have been 'flooded' (ie drowned) until the later 1800s and then to have had a 'chequered history of grazing, as well as a forty year spell when parts were used to grow watercress'. The commercial production of watercress died out in the mid twentieth century but the plant continues to flourish in the shallow flowing water. The reserve is now grazed by Belted Galloway cattle, a rare breed, which thrive on the rough coarse vegetation of the 'marshy fen, the damp woodland and wet meadows' and help to maintain a rich mixture of plant life. Thus the historic floated meadows take on a new life of environmental conservation.

Hare Street

This is a couple of kilometres west of Pewsey at GR 142604 and is an example of many small sites to be seen, even at a casual glance, from the valley roads. At this point there is a a tiny unnamed tributary running underneath the minor road shown as Hare Street, eventually to join the upper eastern Avon some 1500m to the south east near East Sharcott. At right angles to the road on the right when travelling south, the vegetation clearly shows the classic pattern of ridges with their carriers and the interlocking drains. The latter feed a tail drain parallel to Hare Street. This flows into the main watercourse just before it disappears into the culvert under the road.

LOWER WOODFORD

The text and diagrams below are the first of four sets (Woodford, Harnham, Charlton, Downton) which are, with very slight editing changes, exactly as first published (Cowan 1982b). This monograph, linking the descriptive work derived from documents with the evidence on the ground, appears now to have been groundbreaking and has been widely cited and copied – the Woodford diagrams in particular. The author was surprised (but mildly flattered) to discover that the material was being used by DEFRA and more than one adult college.

This example at Lower Woodfood is on the upper Avon some three miles above Salisbury. It is included partly because it is a good example of what is typical or normal – insofar as such terms can apply to hundreds of systems all with their own big or tiny differences. Secondly, when first recorded in 1980 it was still working, as remains the case. It was recently (2004) possible to see from the road that the carriers and drains had been freshly cut and were flowing. The site has also been used in recent years for some of the scientific work discussed elsewhere in this work.

Because in 1980 this Lower Woodford system was being worked in traditional fashion there was no need to use early surveys. The record was guided by the then current Ordnance Survey material and informed by walking the ground with notebook and camera. The diagrams are illustrative rather than accurate or to scale. This is a 'classic' system within a shallow bend of a sinuous river. However the main carriage runs for its complete length so that, unusually, the tail drains from its right hand side have to be taken under it to reach the river.

This system is outlined in Figure 2.5 and references are to the numbered points in that figure. Most of the area can be seen clearly from one or other of the roads running along the valley and from the footpath across it. A good panoramic view is obtained from some points on the eastern road, most usefully

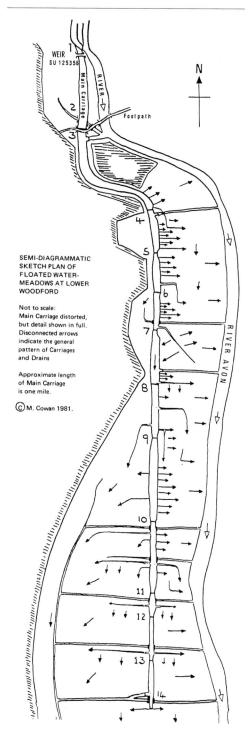

SEMI-DIAGRAMMATIC
SKETCH PLAN OF
FLOATED WATER-
MEADOWS AT LOWER
WOODFORD

Not to scale:
Main Carriage distorted,
but detail shown in full.
Disconnected arrows
indicate the general
pattern of Carriages
and Drains

Approximate length
of Main Carriage
is one mile.

© M. Cowan 1981.

2.5 Lower Woodford water meadow system

when the system is drowned. From the western road a clear view can be had of some of the detail and this is most useful when the system is dry.

The system appears to be part of that dated (VCH 6, p.225) as circa 1665. It lies in a long loop of the River Avon above and below the village of Lower Woodford. It is bounded on the east by the river and on the west by successively, the village, the road and rising ground. The spine of the system, which leaves the river under a footbridge at Point 1, is the main carriage. The flow of water into this is controlled by the weir at Point 1 which can be used to control the river flow. This hatch is of three wooden paddles operated by iron ratchets and set between stone piers. The drop, when water is fully diverted into the main carriage, is some three feet, representing also the total fall over the whole system.

Point 2 is the first of a series of culverts under the main carriage to allow the water used in the field on the right hand side to flow back to the river. This field and the narrow strip on the left between the main carriage and the river are now disused parts of the upstream system. Point 3, below the footpath, is a hatch with one paddle providing a spillway for surplus water back to the river.

The system becomes live at Point 4, with the first of a series of

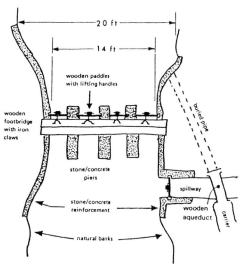

2.6 *Detail of Hatch 4*

hatches on the main carriage which enable the intervening sections to be isolated. In the early part of the year there is usually enough water coming down the river to enable most of the system to be drowned at once. At other times water may have to be used more sparingly and only one part flooded at a time. In the past the needs of others up and down stream have also had to be considered. The hatch at Point 4, typical of all those on this main carriage, is of four paddles; some are of three and at the lower end they are of only one. None has any mechanical movement, each wooden paddle being held in a desired position by means of an iron claw. The area to the left of Point 4 is enlarged in Figure 2.7.

By lowering the paddles at the next lower hatch a section of the main carriage can be filled so that the water spills into the carriers. These are trenches cut along the top of the ridges from which the water spills down the sides, or panes, to create the moving film required. In this case the carriers are at right angles to the main carriage and fed directly from it; there are many other possible configurations. The rate of flow into the carriers and along their length can be controlled, if the gradient requires it, by stops of turf put in or taken out by the drowner. The water is recovered in drains or trenches cut along the bottom of each furrow between the ridges and which, in this case, lead directly back to the river; again there are many possible configurations.

Immediately below the hatch at Point 4 there is a further spillway to the river controlled by a single-paddle hatch which has no controlling devices; when down it is held in position by the pressure of water in the main carriage. Immediately above the main carriage hatch a piped culvert carries water to a small wooden box section aqueduct over the spillway to feed some carriers, Figure 2.7. This characteristic of feeding carriers down stream from a hatch recurs in a variety of forms although the use of an aqueduct in this fashion is unusual.

The remaining characteristic to note at this point is the 'Bow and Arrow' configurations of some carriers and drains. This is a common form that does not actually feature in the field chosen (Figure 2.8) to illustrate the variety of forms that carriers can take.

Dimensions at this point are fairly typical and some are shown in Figure 2.6. Filled carriers give a false impression of their width because of the profile caused by water spilling over the edges. In disused systems both carriers and drains rapidly become grassed over and the ground is blurred into a misleadingly smooth ridge and furrow pattern.

From point 4 to 14 the complete detail of the main carriage is shown including all the water courses fed directly by it. Beyond this the general lie of carriers and drains is shown by disconnected arrows. The area between Points 10 and 11 is enlarged in Figure 2.8.

At Point 6 some of the area down stream to the left of the hatch is fed from above it. Up stream of the hatch at point 7 there is a tail drain under the main carriage and then a diagonal carriage feeding the system to the left. The term tail drain is explained below. The term carriage is here used to describe a water course that is not supplied direct from the river and is thus not a main carriage but nonetheless does not itself normally spill the water over its own edges. Its function is to feed carriers.

At Point 8 there are the remains of a footbridge which appears as if it may have been a hatch at one time. Local information is that it was not but it is now used to divert water into the carriage immediately above it. Further up stream there is a single-paddle hatch controlling a spillway.

Below Point 8 the whole system widens. So far it has largely been confined to the left of the main carriage and drains have recovered water directly into the the river. Down stream from here the drains on the right feed tail drains which in turn recover water to the river, running through culverts under the main carriage at points 10,11,13 and 14 in order to do so. It is not clear whether the tail drain leaving the south-west corner of Figure 2.5 eventually becomes a carriage for a lower now disused section but it would be

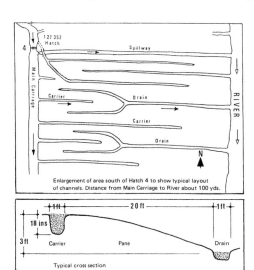

Enlargement of area south of Hatch 4 to show typical layout of channels. Distance from Main Carriage to River about 100 yds.

Typical cross section

2.7 *Detail of meadow at point 4*

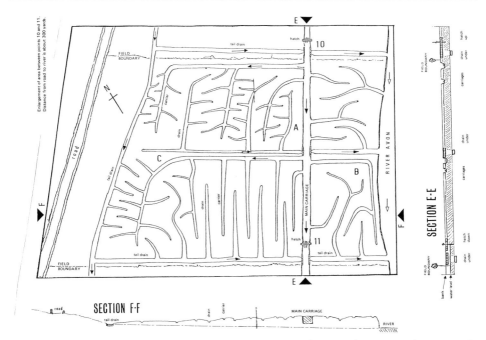

2.8 Enlargement of area between points 10 and 11. Distance from road to river is about 300 yds.

consistent with Davis's generalised description. There is an independent tail
drain between points 10 and 11.

Below Point 11 the main carriage narrows until at Point 14 it is about a
quarter of its original width. Any residual water not required below the carriage
formed by the T junction is drained off at the single-paddle hatch controlling the
spillway into the tail drain at Point 14.

The area between Points 10 and 11 enlarged in Figure 2.8 shows more
clearly the hierarchy of water courses - main carriage, carriage, carrier, drain
and tail drain. However the definition of each has to be qualified. While carriages
of not usually spill direct on to panes they do here – for example at Point A from
the main carriage and point B from a carriage; and at Point C a carriage spills
directly into an adjacent tail drain without any intervening drain.

The sections through this area shown in Figure 2.8 indicate the very slight
gradient from the north to south but the greater drop from west to east to enable
the taildrains to pass under the main carriage.

The main carriage, the banks and the bottom of which are natural for
most of its length, is reinforced with dressed stone and sometimes brick above
and below the hatches and where tail drains pass under it. The culverts carrying
these appear to be of rectangular section and generally of stone construction.

The main carriage, when full, resembles a small river (Figure 2.5 has unnaturally straightened it) and the tail drains look like normal field ditches especially when they run alongside the hedges. Only the carriers and drains appear more obviously unusual man-made features, particularly when recently emptied.

GREAT WISHFORD

The piece that follows was first published in Hatcher Review 14 *(Cowan 1982b, pages 179-187) and is reproduced with only minor editorial changes. It illustrates the thinking that can be called for in trying to decipher a long disused system. In this case a local resident was interested in the so called aberrant stones discussed as the third of the 'mysteries' implied by the original title 'Mysterious Meadows' - and who also, fortuitously, had access to the archives of the local fishing club. To the best of the author's knowledge however no-one has yet (2004) ventured any response to the various and generally speculative suggestions.*

Introduction

The purpose is to consider some unusual aspects of the small system which lies astride the parish boundary between Stapleford and Great Wishford. It is illustrated in the sketch plan (Figure 2.9) which is constructed mainly from the 1901 or second edition of the Ordnance Survey 1:2500 map. The 1925 edition shows virtually the same detail but that for 1976 omits almost all traces of the system. These maps, and others, contain some of the evidence to be used in considering what may be defined as the three mysteries; those of the Non-existent Hatches; the Impossible Carriers; and the Aberrant Stones.

The Great Wishford System is (or was) basically conventional. In its original form it took water from the River Till at Points 1 and 2 and from the River Wylye at Point 3. Hatches (commonly referred to on maps as 'sluices') at these points controlled the flow into main carriages from which it eventually ran into carriers along the top of each parallel ridge. Along the length of each carrier the water overflowed down the sloping sides into drains in the intervening hollows, then possibly into a tail drain and eventually back into a lower point on the river. Detail of the system fed from Point 1 is virtually lost and the main carriage itself has been altered by modern drainage ditches.

From Point 2 the second main carriage supplies Field A. The carriers here run at right angles to the main carriage and they, together with corresponding

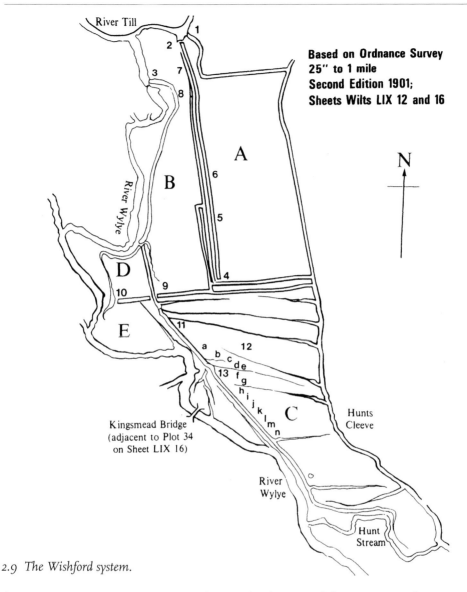

2.9 *The Wishford system.*

drains can still just be traced on the northerly part of the system and running along the east side of the field. This, referred to as Hunt's Cleeve* is immediately below the steeply rising ground to the east and ends in a confluence with the Hunt Stream at the south east corner of the whole system. The 1901 map shows this second main carriage as stopping at the southern end of the field at

---

* The word 'cleeve' is defined in the Oxford Dictionary as a cliff or steep slope and is so understood locally. But the term as used by the Wilton Fly Fishing Club seems to have referred to the tail drain below the cliff and, in that sense, appears on the Club's map of 1953.

Point 4 but it must have had an outflow through a hatch and perhaps a culvert into the tail drain along the south side of the field that rose near Point 7 and drains Field B. Here we have the first mystery of the 'Non-existent Hatches'; and some discussion is appropriate on when the meadows ceased to be drowned.

Non-Existent Hatches

Many floated systems appear on the large scale maps in complete detail down to each individual carrier, hatch and drain. That this is not always so, including here, may indicate variable standards of surveying or that in some cases the system had been out of active use long enough before the survey for the detail to have eroded beyond worthwhile recording.

Some interesting evidence about the discontinuance in the Wishford/ Stapleford area is provided by the Drowners' Dinner which used to be held annually by the Wilton Fly Fishing Club. Those attending, whose goodwill was clearly important to the Club, were those, usually farm workers, who helped maintain the rivers and the system. The numbers seem to have dropped during the 1930s but a dinner is recorded as having been held in 1939 and in 1940 the club records, not a dinner, but gratuities. This suggests therefore that there were at least some systems operating in some form up to the late 30s.

Mr Eric Mundy, a local resident, can recall working for his father's building firm in the early 1920s supplying wooden planks for the fishing club to bridge the ends of the drains on the east side of the Field C where they emptied into Hunt's Cleeve. His recollection is that the field had not then been drowned for many years. Indeed this was why the drains needed to be bridged for the benefit of those fishing Hunt's Cleeve because the untended drains (as is still very apparent) spread and became swampy. This recollection provides a useful 'no later than' date of c.1920 for the abandonment of drowning Field C and possibly Field A.

Returning to the question of the hatches in Field A the problem arises from the fact that the 1901, 1925 and 1976 maps all omit the three hatches of which substantial remains are actually to be found at Points 4, 5 and 6. They have a curiously modern, slightly amateurish look at odds with the style and workmanship usually found and they appear to be later additions to the system. Those at Points 4 and 5 bear the mark, 'C.C 1879', impressed in the concrete facing (at point 4 it appears in two places and at Point 5 it survives in only one, partly masked by a later upstream channel wall.) Thus they seem to post-date the 1877 survey on which the 1901 and 1925 maps are based. The lack of detail on the earlier map taken together with the state of the remains and Mr Mundy's recollection suggests that the system might have been abandoned before the 1877 survey. Why then build new hatches?

One suggestion is that the abandoned main carriage, or at least a short stretch of it between Points 4 and 5, was turned into a 'stew' or breeding tank for fish. Although the Wilton Fly Fishing Club, formed earlier, only moved to the River Wylye in about 1891/2 it was a small and very exclusive club that would only have been attracted to good facilities. Local recollection is that the fishing was originally managed by the occupant of the nearby country house at Druid's Lodge, so C.C. may possibly have been Cecil Chubb, donor of Stonehenge.

If the 'stew' theory is unsound then perhaps the hatches at Points 4 and 5 were constructed in 1879, not for any such novel purpose, but actually to replace earlier ones which had been missed by the 1877 survey. In this case drowning of Field A continued, perhaps well into this century. At Point 6 however the hatch is almost certainly a very much later addition; more a barrage than a hatch, it is set square across the main carriage rather than in the conventional way of steadily narrowing the channel to the point where a wooden paddle could be inserted. The gap here is about 5 feet, far too wide for the normal wooden paddle and suggesting the insertion of separate planks horizontally between the grooves. [Since this was written a similar structure has been identified at Harnham where 'drop boards' are used to close an acqueduct]. None of the three hatches appear on a Wilton Fly Fishing Club map dated 1892, although like the later Ordnance Survey maps this must derive from the 1877 survey. However the two at Points 4 and 5 appear on an undated and unattributed map in a volume (bound 1952) held by the Club. This map also shows the main carriage from Point 1 filled for much of its length with the conventional sign for reeds, indicating that it was choked and disused. The supposition therefore is that if this map, as it must almost certainly be, is a post 1925 edition the hatch (or barrage) at Point 6 is a very late construction concerned with water control but not drowning. So much for the hatches in Field A.

Returning to the top of the system the largest of the three main carriages leaves the River Wylye at Point 3. This main carriage, feeding Fields B and C, has been almost completely filled in by material dredged from the river and its course, now grassed over, is only in one or two places distinguishable. However, the main hatch from the river and some small part of the stone retaining walls adjacent to it are still intact. The actual hatch, unusually for one of this size, is wholly of wood. There are five conventional paddles set between square wooden uprights rather than between stone piers. Such a large wooden construction is certainly unlike most to be seen on the lower Nadder or Avon rivers. There are, as would be expected, the marks for ironwork used in raising the paddles on the footbridge spanning the width of the hatch.

The line of the former main carriage is now crossed at about Point 8 by a modern drain into which the former main carriage from Point 2 has been diverted. It then went on to feed Fields B and C before being deflected sharply east by the Hunt Stream which, as a natural water course, predated it. It is not now clear how the taildrain running across the southern ends of Fields D and A actually worked. The detail at Point 10 is very slightly different on a 1925 map showing a very unlikely configuration, suggesting long disuse during which the pattern of the surviving Impossible Carriers water courses had been changed.

Impossible Carriers

The two parallel water courses running east from Point 11 are, as drawn, clearly spillways designed to carry overflow water from the main carriage back to the river. In this case though, spillways would be constructed much more economically and logically to the west of the main carriage. Furthermore, by standing high on the slope to the east, some short carriers can be seen running on a north/south axis between them which must have been fed from one and drained into the other, making them a very unusual, if not impossible configuration. It seems very possible therefore that they were converted from carrier and /or drain into spillways at some stage before they appear in their present form on the Wilton Fly Fishing Club map dated 1892. On this map they are strongly defined (far more so than on any Ordnance Survey map) and coloured in blue as part of the general river system. Their purpose may have been to maintain the flow of water into Hunt's Cleeve. Although now overgrown, it is known that c.1920, this was being fished and the indication is that as early as 1892 it was necessary to replace the water denied by the fact that Fields A and C were not being drowned.

Aberrant Stones

This final mystery of the 'Aberrant Stones' is the most visible. Of standard pattern and proportions but widely differing dimensions, these stones seem to defy explanation. Unfortunately we cannot now reconstruct either from the map or on the ground the exact configuration of all the carriers and drains in this field.

There are indications (the north-south carriers of the top corner; an odd configuration sometimes shown by cattle churning the softer ground in former drains at Point 12) which suggest that it was not quite as simple as the still obviously visible north-west/ south-east axis might indicate. This is of some relevance when trying to decide why the stones are there.

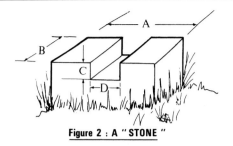

Figure 2 : A " STONE "

FIGURE 1 reference	FROM PREVIOUS STONE (YDS)	DIMENSIONS (INS)				INCISED NUMBER
		A	B	C	D	
a		30	12	4½	6	I
b	9	32+	13	6	5½	II
c	30	35	12	10½	14½	III
d	14	36½	14	8½	15½	IIII
e	7	52	12	12	19	V
f	8	51	10	10	22½	VI
G	20	53	11	8½	24½	VII
h	11	31	12	11½	13	VIII
i	9	28	12	5½	4	IX
j	10	26	10½	5½	4	X
k	8	30	10	6+	9½	?
l	5	35	11	6½	6	XII
m	20	?	?	10½	18+	?
n	5	54	9+	10	26	?
o	93	?	?	13	17+	?

2.10 *Dimensions of the stones.*

There are 15 stones visible and more were probably lost when the main carriage was filled. The dimensions vary but all are of the same shape, illustrated in Figure 2.10. These various dimensions are set out in the table. Most appear to be in their original positions and sit on top of ridges on the line of the carrier in each case. Bearing in mind that the contours of ridge and furrow have been flattened, perhaps for more than a century, it seems likely that originally they were set in the carriers. They are numbered with Roman numerals in sequence from north to south and seem clearly to have been prepared for their own particular sites – very approximately indicated by Points 'a' to 'o' in Figure 2.19. Why?

Stone work in carriers (as opposed to carriages) is rare and usually supports a footpath or cartway so that men or wagons could cross without damaging them. In this case the line of the stones is somewhat eccentric for a footpath and in any case one ran along the western bank of the main carriage. For a cart track the line is equally odd and one would expect to see 2 stones in position at each point (and the other way up) in order to form position at each point (and the other way up) in order to form arches at each end of a culvert. However to be effective any such trackway must bridge drains as well as carriers which is not the case here.

There is no indication of date. The inner face are square cut and do not appear worn. The only clue is that the fourth stone is numbered in the form IIII rather than IV which may mean earlier rather than later and perhaps before 1800. In common with most floated systems in the Wylye Valley this one probably dates from the earlier part of the 17th century but these stones do not look that old. Were they therefore a later addition to check some malfunctioning of the system?

They are all distant, to varying extents, from the line of the main carriage and seem most likely to have been set at varying points along each carriage. It is however particularly difficult to reconcile the widely varying dimensions of the 'cut' in each stone with a sensible pattern of carriers with corresponding dimensions. A clinching argument would be other examples in a clearer context. The farmer concerned would have been a tenant of the Wilton Estate but their muniments tend to be accessible by year rather than field and without even a glimmer of a date any evidence will come to light by accident rather than by design.*

Conclusion

The other mysteries are perhaps more susceptible to solution as has been suggested. The evidence seems to point to drowning having ceased very early - perhaps before 1877, quite likely before 1892. But some of the water courses continued to be maintained after either date (possibly with new hatches to make a 'stew') for reasons connected with fishing. 1877 or even 1892 seem early dates for drowning to have ceased although it is compatible with the generally held view that the floated systems began to decline in the last few decades of the 19th century. There is also plentiful evidence that many systems remained in full use until very recently. Local opinion in Wishford is that the systems generally survived to the 1930s but this is not unanimous nor does it exclude the possibity that particular systems became disused earlier.

---

* After the above had been drafted in 1982 the author's attention was drawn to a map in the Wiltshire Record Office (WRO 451/374) which can be dated 1845 and which deals with a land dispute involving Field C. The nature of the dispute is not known, but the map clearly shows the pattern of the carriers; some of those running east from the main carriage are numbered 1 to 21 from north to south. No other parts of the system are numbered. There is an obvious correlation between the numbered carriers and the pattern of surviving stones. The suggestion that the stones were set in the carriers is strengthened and it is a possibility that they are related to the land dispute. Another straw to be grasped at is the existence of plot marker stones at North Meadow, Cricklade (Whitehead 1982). However, these are set in a grid-like pattern at the corners of plots.

Memories of course are of variable accuracy and maps, particularly early ones, are not always reliable. However the various 1:2500 editions can clearly provide some interesting insights into the decline of floated systems over the last century or so. They might be used in conjunction with fieldwork, in a major study of this decline - a task not yet undertaken. If so a useful by-product would be the recording of more actual data about particular systems and the improvement of the detailed record of a fast disappearing feature of the local countryside.

HARNHAM

The description below was published in 1982 (Cowan 1982a) and is reproduced with six new paragraphs of introduction and a few added points, indicated in square brackets.

The system, on the lowest reach of the River Nadder before its confluence with the River Avon, was originally chosen as a slightly unusual example of floated meadows. Because of the way that the River Nadder splits into two channels around what is, in effect, a tear drop shaped island the 'classic ' layout, as exemplified at Lower Woodfood, is not possible. This has in turn resulted in unusual solutions.

Both channels of the river had mills which together had to provide the head of water needed for drowning. Their respective water supplies had to be coordinated with the needs of a number of different operators who drowned the intervening meadows. There are, unusually, multiple offtakes from the river above the mills which in a variety of ways feed the whole of the 'island' .There are thus a number of interesting archaeological features with, for example carriages crossing drains by means of aqueducts or inverse syphons. Finally, most features are visible from the the well used Town Path that bisects the 'teardrop' across its widest point.

The diagrammatic outline of the Harnham system (Figure 2.11) is also as drawn and published in 1982. The broad outline was taken from early ordnance Survey work predating the removal of Fisherton Mill and the reconstruction of the north tip of the site to accommodate houses on the modern named Fisherton Island. The remainder of the detail was from observation and pacing on the ground. As an outline, this remains valid and is included here to present a complex system simply.

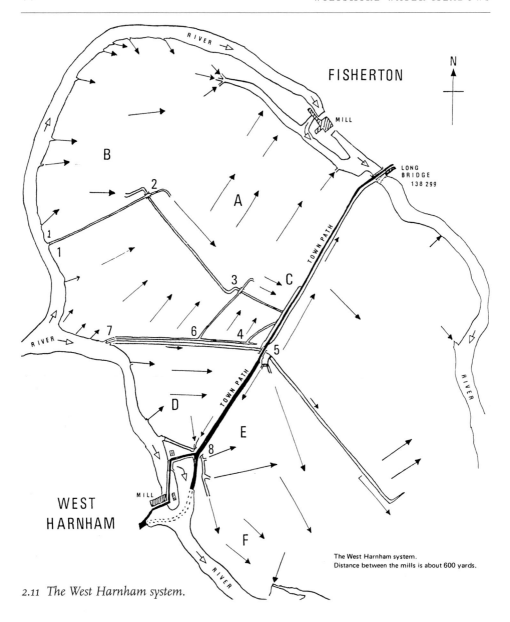

2.11 *The West Harnham system.*

Research in more recent years, using the 1787 enclosure map, late
nineteenth Ordnance Survey maps, known details of some Victorian
reconstruction and general archaeological observation, has brought to light
substantial detail of ownership, tenancies, mead names and the finer detail of
the structure and layout of the irrigation system. There is no known documentary
evidence to date the original construction but it clearly long predates enclosure
in the late eighteenth century. A contract of 1669 mentions water meadows at

Parsonage Farm, West Harnham, which may or may not have included the island site, but all the general indicators suggest the early to mid seventeenth century. Some of this material is incorporated in the commentary on the Town Path treated as a Valley Crossing in Chapter 4.

This 'island' site is the surviving fragment of extensive (and quite normal) floated meadows across the width of the lower Nadder valley. The remainder have been built over, to the north of the river by the growth of Salisbury to the west; and south of the river by the development of East and West Harnham. What are now called the Harnham meadows, as an island, have been and remain relatively inaccessible. They are valued as one of the 'green fingers' created by the rivers that reach towards the heart of the city and have protected status as a Site of Special Interest (SSSI).

The Harnham Water Meadows Trust was created in 1991 to purchase, restore and manage the last 50 acres of the site remaining in private hands, the Dean and Chapter of Salisbury Cathedral having owned a further 38 acres since 1931. The latter were leased to the Trust in 2002 and the 88 acres (the whole island except for a small area at the tip) are now managed as a single entity. There is a continuing programme of restoration, rebuilding hatches ,digging out irrigation watercourses and attempting some very occasional and limited drowning of the more accessible parts for demonstration purposes. For this, these meadows are ideally placed, accessible and easily visible although drowning is difficult because the modern river level is lower than in the past. The Trust, and its Friends organisation is also developing a computer aided mapping system to be able to present the detail of the system more clearly and informatively both in print and on its web site.

Apart from a small element at the south end Figure 2.11 covers the 'Island' formed by two arms of the River Nadder (also see Figure 4.1 for later, further, interpretation). Fisherton and Harnham Mills (the former now replaced by two weirs) pre-date the system and their position thus determined the lowest points from which water could be drawn. The notable features therefore illustrate how the designers chose to carry water over an unusually wide system with virtually no drop to either east or west and a conventional fall of two or three feet over the north/south distance. Dimensions of hatches and water courses in this system are generally similar to those at Lower Woodford.

As at Lower Woodford there is a need to run drains under carriages. The solutions are quite different. There is at Harnham one obvious visible main carriage passing under the mid point of the Town Path but this actually only feeds part of the system to the south of that path. There is another less obvious main carriage at Point 8 feeding the remainder of the south side which passes under the path at the Harnham end; and several other smaller main carriages, mostly now lost, around the northern perimeter of the 'Island'.

These latter were all controlled by single paddle hatches [in fact one is double] on the river and were thus much smaller than one would normally expect of a main carriage. The hatches and their stone piers together with short stretches of stone or concrete or walled channel have now mostly been filled in with silt dredged from the river bed in the course of routine maintenance. One, still partly visible, leaves the river at Point 1 and eventually feeds area A [now generally dug out and rebuilt – see Figure 4.1]. To reach this it is carried over the tail drain from area B by what the maps show as an 'aqueduct' at Point 2. At this point [the] carriage is a concrete box section some nine feet wide [grooved for drop boards] with, at right angles under it, an eighteen inch pipe for the drain [now identified as an inverse syphon].

This taildrain continues to Point 3 where it is again crossed by an 'aqueduct' before joining the spillways from Points 4 and 5, turning north-east, passing under the Town Path and rejoining the river. This second aqueduct is unusual and consists of a square section (side 32 inch) iron trough fourteen feet in length bridging the drain between stone piers. On the west side it has an oval plate [now lost] inscribed 'J Armitage - Maker - Fisherton Iron Works - Salisbury' [Probably made after 1842, when the business does not appear in Pigot's directory: Rogers and Chandler 1992]. [The curious configurations at Points 2 and 3 reflect areas in different ownership, and change in the mid nineteenth century. On the ground the detail at Point 2 is more complex than it is drawn. Here the aspect to note is that, most unusually, carriages and drains that would normally be expected to run straight, curve round corners almost at right angles, the vulnerable inner bank reinforced by stone lining.]

The water course crossing the aqueduct is a carriage in that it is carrying water for area C but it also acted as a carrier and spilled water along its own length. It was controlled at Point 6 either by a wooden hatch that has disappeared or by a turf stop [a small wooden paddle has now been put in place]. Point 6 is on a narrow main carriage (now only a shallow depression) running close beside the wider main carriage which is still used as a river overflow. Both were controlled by adjacent hatches on the river at Point 7 but the brick and stone lined channel of the former has been filled in. The ruins [now restored] of the wider three-paddle hatch are best seen from the other side of the river (from Middle Street playing field) [both hatches have been restored]. From Point 5 this wider of the two central main carriages, having passed under the Town Path, formerly divided in four directions of which three remain.

At Point 8 the other larger main carriage runs under the Town Path (Figure 2.12) and, at that same point, over the taildrain, from area D. It then immediately splits into three, two carriages supply areas E and F while the main carriage itself turns east and then south to supply the far end of the system (out of the Figure) in conjunction with the other main carriage from Point 5.

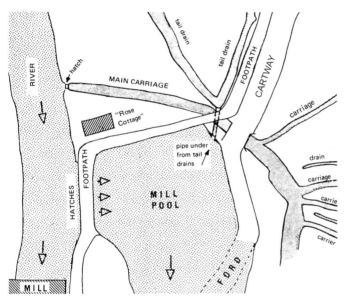

2.12 *Left: Enlargement of the area around point 8, with (centre right) the three-tier structure of footpath and cartway crossing the main carriage and this, in turn, crossing the tail drain. Below left: View from the cartway bridge to the north-west, cathedral to left and llama centre stage. Below right: Cartway bridge with wooden railings, footpath with metal railings and (bottom right) water glinting in the tail drain visible through the arched channel under the aqueduct.*

SALISBURY TO DOWNTON

Some aspects of this section are covered in more depth in Chapter 5

Topography

The valley of the lower Avon between the road crossings at Salisbury and Downton forms a rough rectangle some 6 miles long and up to a mile or so wide running slightly south east from Salisbury. The river meanders sinuously from side to side. The chalk valleys usually have a highway of some sort along each side, at the foot of the downs but just above the valley floor. It is equally usual for one route to have become more developed than the other. The lower Avon is no exception.

On the left (or east) side the road actually starts from Salisbury as the main A36 but soon forks to the right as the minor Witherington Road through Alderbury, skirting Trafalgar and Barford parks to Downton. On the right the valley is strongly defined by the modern A338. The two routes are linked at Salisbury by the river crossings of the old Ayleswade and New Harnham Road bridges. At Downton the main street (The Borough) crosses a major carriage, the river and a mill tail. Between Salisbury and Downton there were, historically, three crossings. One remains as a minor footpath without the ferry which crossed the river. There is a private road crossing at Longford Castle and a usable footpath from Charlton to Standlynch Mill dealt with in detail below.

History

This area has been selected as an illustration for several reasons. The systems are of clear seventeenth century origin. They are, compared with anything upstream, massive and needed relatively enormous investment and engineering effort. There is substantial archaeology. One system still operates in the traditional manner and has provided the base for much of the renewed scientific and environmental interest of the last decade or so. Possibly most important however is the recent publication of documentary evidence (Steele 1982;Betty 1999, 2004). All quotations and all the seventeenth century names and dates are from the 2004 work.

This 'adds to the existing literature by describing a remarkable project for creating some 250 acres of water meadows along a four-mile stretch of the river Avon.... started in 1665 and finished in 1690'. This was based on creating two

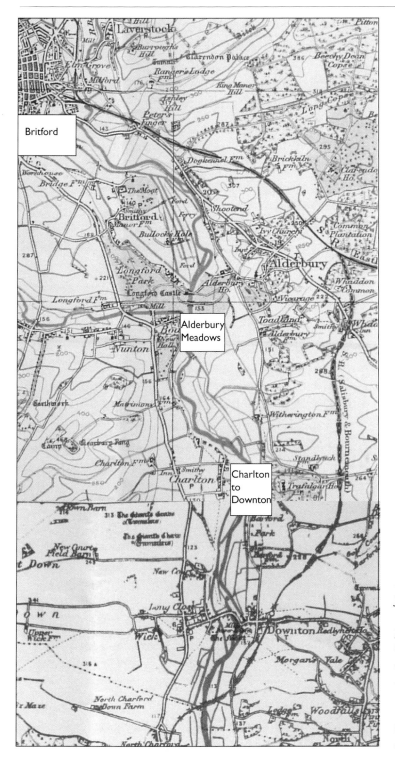

Britford

Alderbury Meadows

Charlton to Downton

2.13 Avon valley from Salisbury to Downton. Key points are Britford systems (Figure 2.14), Alderbury Meadows system (Figure 2.15), and Charlton to Downton systems (Figure 2.16).

new massive main carriages, one starting from the Alderbury Meadows near
Bodenham, the other at Charlton each some 24 feet wide. It was driven through
by a remarkable vigorous and far seeing 'yeoman', John Snow. He was steward
at Downton for Sir Joseph Ashe, a London merchant and one of the two Members
of Parliament for Downton. Sir Joseph lived in Twickenham and continually
complained at the costs of the project which, on completion in 1690 amounted
to some £5000 or about £20 for each acre of floated meadow created. In fact
this figure was much in line with that given by Thomas Davis (1794) 'although
he, no doubt, was thinking of much less ambitious schemes'.

Economics

Such a large scheme appears therefore to have produced no economy of scale
but, despite what we might today call continuous cost over-runs, Snow organized
both the construction work and the many legal agreements at a cost that led to
the increases in the land value that was expected. 'The value of the meadows was
doubled as a result of the watering. In 1628 and again during the 1650s the
meadows at Witherington, Standlynch and New Court were valued at £1 per
acre. By 1682 the unwatered meadows remained at £1, but the watered meadows
were said to be worth £2 an acre.....early grass and reliable crops of hay provided
by the water meadows meant that more livestock could be kept and increased
crops of wheat and barley could be grown, increasing the value of the whole
farm'. On Sir Joseph Ashe's death in 1686 the larger part of New Court Farm
was valued at £420 per annum 'naturally' but £520 'with the improvement''.
The comparable figures for Witherington Farm were £122 and £187.

Despite the huge costs other landowners were apparently prompted to
follow Joseph Ashe's example. In 1676 Lord Coleraine, owner of Longford Castle
and two others combined to create a system based on diverting water from above
Nunton Paper Mill on the river Ebble shortly before it joins the Avon as Salisbury's
fifth river. In the 1680s the meadows at Britford were floated when Thomas
Jervois built 'a weir . . . across the Avon', although there are some references
indicating earlier work. Thus the Salisbury to Downton 'rectangle' was, with the
exception of the Longford Castle park, completely filled with floated meadow
systems.

Locations

The approach in this piece is to start with the modern Ordnance Survey map
and identify the 'start points ' of the seven identifiable systems that occupy the

Salisbury Downton rectangle. (Figure 2.13) These are three at Britford, one at
Nunton, and three towards Downton, two of them created by Ashe and Snow.
Each will be described very briefly but the main focus will be at the mid point,
the Charlton-Standlynch crossing.

For the three Britford systems (Figure 2.14) the necessary head of water
in the river below Harnham Bridge is provided by the Thomas Jervois's 'weir'

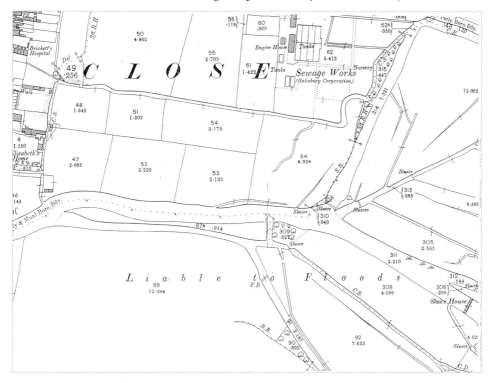

2.14 **Control of Britford systems** *This is part of the 1901 edition 1:2500 Ordnance Survey.*
Some of the printed numbers showing land divisions (lots) or areas (in acres) are used here to
identify features on the River Avon as it flows from left to right on the figure, west to east on the
ground. From the centre of the valley it turns sharply north past the former sewage works, then
south west. The river is identifiable by the dotted line of the parliamentary and municipal
boundaries.

There are three control points. First, the water course parallel to the river below the long
spit of land marked 87a is the Avon Navigation. This feeds a main carriage (on the line of a
parish boundary) between 308 and 92 before turning right towards Britford to feed the Britford
west meadows. Further downstream on the Avon are traces of a disused system on what is now
Churchill Gardens, including the first sluice marked (below 64). Shortly after this the main
weir (assumed to be Sir Thomas Jervois's weir originally of the 1680s) at the corner of the
modern Gardens is not marked as such but identifiable above 310. Immediately after this is the
main carriage, marked 313, which supplies Britford east system within the curve of the river.
Finally there is the leat marked 311 towards the 'Sluice House' at 306 which controls the water
for the mile long main carriage to the Britford central system.

which appears to survive in modern form at the south east corner of Churchill Gardens. (Grid Reference 150291). Here the river turns sharp left and meanders in a wide sweep to run briefly beside the A36 and then behind the car wash, tyre centres and the like; at the B and Q superstore car park it is joined unobtrusively by the river Bourne. This is the fourth of Salisbury's five rivers (waters of the Nadder, Wylye and upper Avon having joined forces further upstream). As we have seen the Ebble, or fifth, joins further down. The lower Avon continues on the left side of the valley and then to the centre, crossing Longford Castle park (Figure 2.15), followed by a long curve back to Standlynch mill on the left (Figure 2.16) and hence to Downton.

From the corner of Churchill Gardens (Figure 2.14) many will assume that the wide watercourse going straight on is the river and the drop over the weir to the left is irrelevant. Indeed, from the map this appears to be the case as it is boldly proclaimed to be so by the Ordnance Survey. However it has to be assumed the words 'River Avon' along the side of what is clearly the artificial leat are meant to embrace the several parallel watercourses. The real course of the river is established by the parish boundary marked along it.

At the far end of this weir is a main carriage feeding the small complex of carriers in this first tight bend of the river (Britford east). The leat, just referred to, continues straight on to the hatches marked on the map as 'Sluice House', a number of hatches and an eel trap within a building bridging the watercouse. This eventually feeds the large complex (Britford centre) in the next long bend of the river. Finally, some four hundred yards back upstream there is, off to the right, the entrance to the short-lived and ill fated Avon Navigation of the 1680s (discussed more fully below) which acts as the somewhat unusual main carriage for the final Britford complex (Britford west).

The 'Navigation' carriage rejoins the river by Longford Castle (173267). The park now interrupts any watering which resumes (within our rectangle) with the small system below Nunton bridge and then the two major Ashe works. The first of these (started in 1665) is fed by the main carriage from the river in Alderbury Meadows (172260) just above the confluence with the Ebble (Figure 2.15). The system finally returns its water to the Avon by several tail drains, principally from that past Witherington Farm to a point just above Standlynch Mill. Then, a little upstream, is the point (177239) where 'in 1675 a second main carriage was begun in order to water the meadows beyond New Court Farm' (and below Downton) on the west side of the valley. Shortly after 1690 a new owner of the Barford Estate created the final (or seventh) system with a main

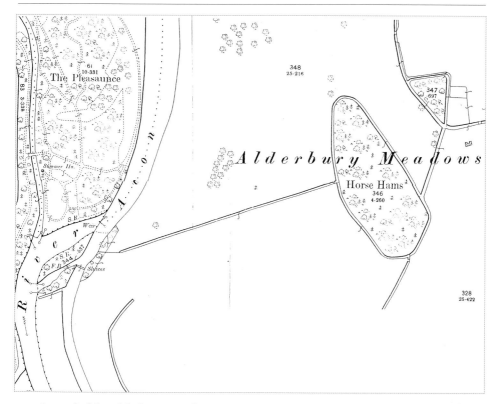

2.15 **Control of the Alderbury Meadows system** *This is part of the 1901 edition 1:2500 Ordnance Survey. The River Avon flows from top to bottom on the figure, north to south on the ground. The section shows some 600 metres, or about half the width, of the valley bottom from its western edge. The Horse Hams copse watercourse, draining west to the Avon and south on the Alderbury Meadows seems to have the characteristics of a landscape feature rather than irrigation.*

The control devices for the Alderbury Meadows system are on the left. The weir to maintain the head of water is marked as the river (with a parish boundary) turns right and begins it long irregular curve to Charlton, containing the second Ashe/Snow system. The watercourse that continues south past a spillway and controlled by further hatches is the great main carriage built in the 1660's and apparently confused on the Naish map as a planned canal cut. To the west through the wooded 'Pleasaunce' of Longford Park is the River Ebble joining the Avon just above the letter v in the word River.

carriage from the east end of Standlynch Mill feeding that side of the valley (Steele 1982).

Charlton to Standlynch crossing

This valley crossing is shown from the 1901 map (Figure 2.14) and diagrammatically (Figure 2.17). The latter, from 1982, illustrates the way in which some features are incorporated in the modern river and agricultural systems while others are rapidly lost once the practice of drowning stops. Most of the features mentioned are visible from the footpath between Charlton and Standlynch.

The area is at the junction of several sections of floated meadow. At Point 1 the tail of the system between Longford and Standlynch rejoins the river. At Point 2 Joseph Ashe's 1675 main carriage leaves the river to feed the systems to the right down to and below Downton. To the right of this main carriage is the taildrain of a system, now largely lost, above and beside Charlton. At Point 3 a main carriage leaves the river beside Standlynch Mill (not under it as stated in VCH XI p 71) to supply the system to the left past Barford as far as Downton.

The taildrain crossed by the western of the two footbridges at Point 4 recovers water from the system between it and Charlton. This must have been fed, at least in part, by a carriage (hierarchical status and start point uncertain) possibly now visible only as a shallow depression running parallel to the fence crossed by the stile at Point 5. There is little indication of this system on any map but it remains, overgrown but traceable on the ground.

The probable line of the carriage does not appear on any map including the largest and earliest based on a survey date of c1874; the whole area is only superficially shown in contrast to the systems up and down stream which are mapped in detail. The tail drain is some three feet below the level of the main carriage running from Point 2 but eventually feeds into it about half a mile down stream below further Hatches.

The flow into this main carriage (which would have been competing for water with that at Point 3 and the mill itself) is controlled by the hatch at Point 2. This has been partly reconstructed but ironwork is marked 'B Dutch/War' [a Warminster Iron foundry; possibly the basis for a widespread myth that floated

---

2.16 (opposite) **Control of the Charlton to Downton systems**. *This is part of the 1901 edition 1:2500 Ordnance Survey. Printed numbers showing land divisions (lots) or areas (in acres) are used here to identify features. The River Avon flows from top to bottom on the figure, north to south on the map. At the first bend below the printed figure 71 there is a complex of sluices including the surviving and significant one marked 'hatches' controlling the second main carriage, completed by about 1680, and supplying water to meadows for some three miles.*

The river continues in a tight double bend joined where it reaches the west side of the valley floor by the final tail drain from the Alderbury meadows. Some 300m downstream the head of water is provided by the identified weir and, further down in the mill leat, a set of hatches. Immediately past these and level with the figure 125 a small building is the eel trap with hatches above. Finally there is Standlynch Mill and squeezed between it and the rising valley side is the last main carriage (identified by the figures 279.471) for the eastern systems as far as Downton.

meadows were the work of Dutch engineers] This marking recurs elsewhere on this main carriage, near New Court Farm.

The general lie of carriers and drains is shown in the Figure and throughout the area they can just be followed on the ground. Below this area the systems on

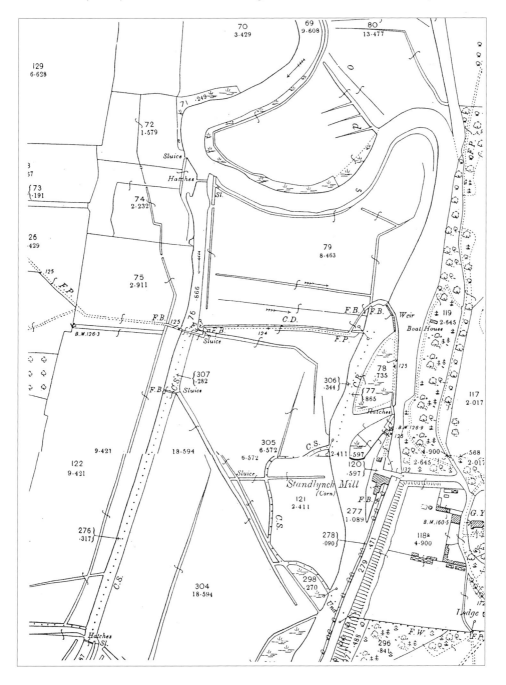

both sides of the river are being lost to development, mainly fish farming but the main carriages controlled by hatches at Points 2 and 3 survive as integral parts of that development.

Dimensions in this system reflect the much greater flow of water in the river below a confluence of the rivers Nadder, Wylye, Ebble and Bourne with the Avon at Salisbury. The main carriages from Points 2 and 3 are up to thirty feet wide; hatches and the ironwork are correspondingly larger and more substantial. The remaining water courses and their controls are of standard dimensions as illustrated at Lower Woodford.

At Point 4 the footpath passes a recent [2004] memorial stile (Dawn's Stile) before crossing the main carriage by a footbridge. Visible a short distance upstream are the hatches (reconstructed but with some early ironwork) controlling the water into this system. From this viewpoint and again further on across the valley the relative magnitude of the work compared to any other previously encountered becomes apparent. For the first time the structures have to cope with the water of all five Salisbury rivers. From the footbridge the present day path runs a short distance between a hedge and a disused tail drain, crosses two small wooden footbridges over more tail drains and reaches the river.

From this point on there are a series of structures that collectively present what is likely to be one of the best archaeological sites of water control structures existing. Immediately upstream is the main weir, curved against the flow of the water, modernized but with nine apertures and surmounted by a narrow wooden footbridge. This is in line with documentary evidence from the 1680s which includes references to the costs and difficulties of building structures with as many as ten 'eyes' or hatches. At the far bank the path runs south alongside the mill leat (on the left) and first passes over an apparently modern stone slab (with a single hatch on each side) bridging the entry to a pond on the right; an exit hatch is visible on the far side of the pond. [This is not on the 1901 map and was not recorded in 1982].

Some yards further on is a set of six traditional wood and iron hatches which appear to complement the nine aperture weir in controlling river flow. This, conceivably, may be a former flash lock. It is followed immediately by a further four hatches controlling water through a substantial brick building housing the eel trap. The path continues to Standlynch Mill with the leat on the left and, some feet below on the right, modern fish farming features and the river. The mill 'had been rebuilt with a new weir and leat in 1575. The effect of

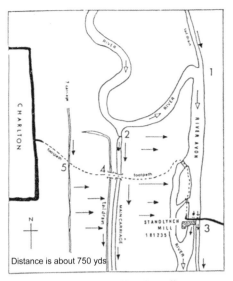

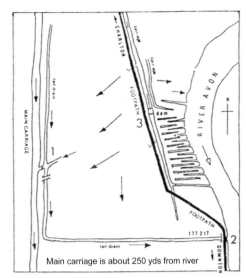

2.17 *Charlton to Standlynch Mill*   2.18 *Part of the Downton system*

the new water courses meant that the mill had to be rebuilt on a new site in 1697'. It remains, in good condition, the near end modernized as a cottage but the working part, (with apparently only one aperture) disused since it ceased in the early twentieth century to generate electricity for Trafalgar House on the hill above. Finally, between the mill and the steep valley side are the nine hatches (three in use) for the final, seventh, system in our Salisbury to Downton rectangle.

Downton detail

Downton is the next main river crossing below Salisbury and provides an opportunity to see some of the work involved in the lower part of the systems being considered. From the west the first bridge is over the main carriage from Charlton. The second is over the river and third crosses the stream below a former tannery. A small part of the system past New Court, accessible from the footpath by the river, is illustrated in Figure 2.18.

The direct footway from Charlton to Downton, joining The Borough at Downton by the River Avon bridge is unlike the paths at Woodford, Harnham and Standlynch which joins settlements on either side of the river. This path is on the same axis at the river and, also unlike the other examples, may have affected the basic design of the system from the point where it crosses the main carriage from Charlton near New Court Farm. [This is the main carriage which originated in Figure 2.17 Point 2]. From this point the path runs diagonally between that main carriage and the river which are roughly parallel.

A carriage left the main carriage at the same point and ran immediately alongside the east side off the path until it reached the river. Only the southern part remains in its original form. In the area illustrated the triangular segment to the west of the path is watered in a normal way; the carriers and drains, mostly still to be traced, running generally south west into a taildrain. Water could then be recovered through a triple hatch, at Point 1, back into the main carriage or, after turning east, under the path and into the river at Point 2. The carriers were fed initially from several culverts (some possibly with a hatch) running under the path.

To the east of the path the system shows two different sets of characteristics above and below a stone dam at Point 3. [more recently visited, this appears actually to be a rubble stop replacing an earlier hatch] Above the dam a single take-off point from the carriage fed a further carriage (thus a third level in the hierarchy) running parallel and to the left of it. This in turn fed carriers and drains from which water was recovered direct to the river.

Below the dam each individual carrier is filled directly through a culvert, known locally as a bunnel. To the unaccustomed eye it looks from the dry system as if water runs from the carrier on top of the ridge, westwards, through the culvert into the carriage rather than the reverse. The section drawing in Figure 2.19 indicates how the water level has to be visualised. The culvert [in fact an inverse siphon] is a pipe of some twelve inch

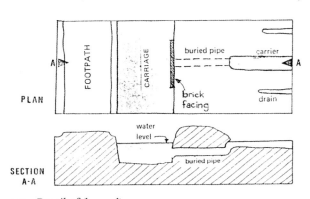

2.19 Detail of 'bunnel'.

diameter set, at the carriage end, in a brick facing. It is not clear why the simpler system north of the dam could not have been used. The maps show the system in fair detail to the west of the path but not at all to the east.

Avon Navigation

Even amongst the oddities and variations to be found in the creation of water meadows the section of the Avon Navigation at Britford is a real anomaly, a failed canal converted to use as the main carriage of a system still operated. The lower parts of the Navigation also pose interesting questions.

The Canal Age flowered in the late eighteenth century but there had been a few earlier attempts during the seventeenth to canalize rivers. One of these was the Hampshire Avon. The process was inaugurated in 1664/5 (by an appropriate Act of Parliament) to improve the Avon, making it navigable for freight traffic from Salisbury to the sea at Christchurch. A major justification for the Act was to improve the supply of coal – a barge would carry as much sea coal as twenty wagons and eighty horses. However words only became action on 20th September 1675 when Bishop Seth Ward, a scientist, man of vision and driving force of the venture, cut the first spit. His vision was not enough, soon after the turn of the century work was effectively abandoned.

However at the same time as canal construction and operation was going on from 1675 to 1715 (Cross 1970), or perhaps a few years later (Chandler 1983), water meadows were being created (1665 – 1690). The interaction of the two processes informs our knowledge of both. Broadly, at Britford the Navigation seems to have come first and the irrigation system was constructed around and making use of it. The floated systems from Alderbury to Downton were complete before canal work, if any, took place.

On all aspects there is accessible published material generally based on documentary or archaeological evidence. First is a well known eighteenth century map of Salisbury with the whole length of the River Avon and ostensibly, its canalized sections (Naish 1716 – but better known for its 1751 edition). There is the first modern summary of the canal story (Willan 1937); a passing unsupported and ambivalent statement that by 1684 25-ton barges 'could' reach Salisbury (Short 1957): and the results of a twelve year survey of what remained of the canal (Cross 1970;also 2003). Next is the first work on the Ashe/Snow floating projects (Steele 1982); a useful summary of canal matters (Chandler 1983); and most recently a thorough reworking of the documents about the Ashe/Snow work and other systems from Britford to below Downton (Bettey 2005).

That there was commercial movement on the canal, at least past Standlynch seems to be well documented. The apparently undocumented claim of barges reaching Salisbury is conceivable. Certainly there is a painting, *Landscape with view of Salisbury Cathedral*, from a viewpoint south of the cathedral with a craft under sail in the middle distance. This is provenanced by the New South Wales Art Gallery as 'eighteenth century' (Cross 2003). The final stage at least was relatively easy given the existence of the Britford cut, clearly visible today as the main carriage for the Britford west meadow system.

Naish's map is mainly concerned with the city but has, on the left and constrained into a narrow vertical strip 'The River Avon between Salisbury and the Sea. Accurately surveyed by Mr Tho Naish and Mr Ja Mooring'. Shown (in dotted lines) but not identified as such are the stretches of canal that cut across long bends and bypass the major obstacles of mills and weirs. The detail apparently reflects the plan drawn by Naish in 1675 (Cross 2003) but as the 1751 edition refers to 'Frowds Hospital built in 1749', some years after both canal construction and attempted operations had stopped, it might be assumed that the canal detail shown still did actually exist at that time. Between Salisbury and Downton three stretches, or cuts, of canal are shown. In the 1960s survey (Cross 1972; and also 2003) the first one from below Harnham Bridge to just above Longford Castle is dealt with in detail but there is no reference to the other two.

A 1974 aerial photograph (Cook et al 2003 online by Wiley Interscience) covers the lowest one third of the Britford cut and shows clearly that it serves as the (most unusual) main carriage for that part of the former Britford west meadow system still active. One of the main hatches providing the necessary head of water has replaced the former top gate of the pound lock further upstream. There is a further similar main hatch nearer to Longford where there may have been another pound lock. The 1901 Ordnance Survey (surveyed 1875) shows more that twenty sluices taking water from along the whole length the Navigation. As a main carriage it is unusual in not become narrower and eventually coming to an end, all of its water returning to the river via drains. In fact, for a floated system it wasted water, but it was there and in the way. No doubt the easiest answer was to make best use of it.

The second cut is shown from below Longford Park on the west side of the valley (marked as Alderbury as the meadows it crosses are so named, but actually much nearer Bodenham) to the east side at Standlynch. The somewhat imprecisely diagrammatic line is suspiciously close to that of the Ashe/Snow main carriage and its eventual tail drain. Similarly, the third cut is shown from Standlynch past New Court Farm and Downton and coincides with the second Ashe/Snow main carriage. Messrs Naish and Mooring appear to have reprinted the original canal plan and confused meadow structures as canal work that never happened. There are certainly two convincing pieces of evidence that what few barges there were used the river from Downton to Longford, using flash or staunch locks to pass Standlynch weir, and by implication, that at Alderbury Meadows as well.

The first record is of a 1737 law suit by the Radnor Estate (Longford Castle) over the creation of the water meadows. Four witness from Standlynch testified that barges had gone 'through the weir gap', that is, by the flash or staunch lock, and that they had come up from Christchurch and down from Salisbury for 'several years together' some 45 years before, perhaps 1690 (Cross 1972, quoting WRO Radnor 490/1683).

Secondly, the Ashe/Snow work had to provide for seventy seven bridges on the west side of the river, ranging from those over 3-4 foot drains to 35 feet over the 'main Cut'. They had to be 'sufficient for men and horses to pass over' to haul barges. There was understanding between the Commissioners governing the Navigation venture and Sir Joseph Ashe. His letters to Snow dealt with the consequences of a canal cut into his existing meadows but was prepared to think about 'a cut through my Manoor on the pasture side'. The bridges are apparently marked on a 1712 map of New Court Farm (Steele 1982 quoting WRO 490/909). If a towpath continued upstream on the west bank if would need either to change banks before Alderbury or cross the Ebble. There is no published evidence or any obvious archaeological indicators about what happened. This part of the Avon valley was rather crowded in the last quarter of the seventeenth century and with two major engineering projects underway there was obvious potential for conflict. Some of the documentary and archaeological record has been unravelled but the picture at present is far from complete.

3
Observation

INTRODUCTION

It is easy to say that the floated water meadows are easily seen, but how can this actually be done? Roads follow the course of a valley, usually on both sides. Normally one will have become more dominant, upgraded and frequently bypassing the villages. Travelling on either side of a valley, at varying heights above the river, can often bring rewarding views of the valley floor and less often, obvious examples of the characteristic ridge and furrow pattern of former irrigation channels. However more often than not these are only glimpses between buildings or through gaps or gates in hedges. To stop or park a car is not easy and to walk on roads that are busy or narrow or both is often hazardous. A better way is to make use of the valley crossings. For example in the ten miles or so of river between Wilton and Downton there are 8 crossings.

Below **Wilton** the A3094 crosses the Wylye and then the Nadder in quick succession just above their confluence as the Nadder. Downstream **Broken Bridges (127133)** footpath links **Bemerton and West Harnham**. This is followed by the very well used **Town Path (138299)** from **West Harnham to Fisherton** (and in effect to Salisbury), dealt with extensively in Chapter 4. Next, **Ayleswade Bridge (144291) in East Harnham** replaced a ford in 1244 and is still there generally unchanged but bypassed in 1931, a hundred yards or so downstream, by the twentieth century dual carriageway A338 **(145292)**. From **Britford to Shute End (174279)** the footpath is abruptly broken by the absence of a ferry that, long ago, completed the crossing. In Longford Castle Park a private road crosses from **Nunton to Alderbury (172267)**. A mile or so on again a footpath (dealt with fully in Chapter 2) connects **Charlton to Standlynch Mill (182237)** and Trafalgar Park. Finally the B3080 makes the crossing at **Downton (177216)**.

Such crossings are rarely more than a mile apart. They usually connect settlements on either side of the valley, in a few cases join two parts of the same settlement and sometimes reflect a need long vanished. This last category tend to have fallen into disuse, but others remain with varying degrees of use and accessibility. Some are footpaths, some were and remain minor roads and some are major highways. A few of these crossings and some other features on each side of Salisbury's five rivers are explored below, clockwise starting with the Ebble. Generally the six figure grid references are an approximation of where the crossing intersects with the actual river.

EBBLE VALLEY

The river rises at Alvediston and flows east to join the Avon, below Salisbury at Nunton. Initially the valley is very narrow and the floor only widens out above **Broadchalke (030252)** where two crossings join the opposite sides of the village. The upper of the two road crossings is the less important as a road but more interesting for evidence of irrigation in that it crosses watercress beds still in active production. There are large rectangular beds bounded by low concrete walls. There are six beds across the 100 metres or so of the flat valley floor immediately above the road: successive rows are eventually reduced to two about 400 metres upstream.

Here the natural flow of the river enters the system and is distributed throughout the beds before being collected again, taken under the two arch road bridge, with interesting early stone work, to repeat the process for the downstream beds. Growing watercress was quite extensively developed in the chalk valleys in the later nineteenth century, adapting the former irrigation systems, suggested here by the other bridge on this short length of road, on the north edge of the valley floor. This has two modern circular culverts but the watercourse is flanked for some metres up and downstream by early stonework indicating the likelihood of an earlier set of hatches.

Below Broadchalke the river curves to the left, or north, and briefly flows beside the road on that side of the valley, the meadows formerly watered by it clearly visible. It then curves the other way, to the south past **Knighton Mill (050254)** (accessible by footpath, more easily from the south, serving modernised mill buildings) and past **Stoke Farthing (052254)**. The valley floor narrows between **Bishopstone** to the north and **Croucheston** to the south and is crossed (065255) by a stretch of no more than a hundred metres or so of the road leading to various culs-de-sac and a footpath.

The irrigated meadows at this point were formerly converted to watercress beds, as at Broadchalke, and production continued into the 1990s before further conversion on a sound environmental basis into the present lakes for leisure fishing. The original pattern of irrigation cannot be determined on the ground although if the early Ordnance Survey maps predate building the watercress beds they could throw some light of the various parts that the three bridges played in the system. There is evidence of early stonework and there are hatches just upstream of the southernmost bridge but the most significant feature of the irrigation archaeology here is simply the existence of three bridges in a very short crossing.

At **Stratford Toney (094263)** the river is crossed by a ford where it curves close to the southern edge of the valley floor, supplemented by a stone and brick footbridge and a modern concrete farm bridge. The road north from the ford then crosses a small bridge with dressed stone abutments. This is over a water course that left the river upstream, past the church, at about **092264** and is likely to have been the main carriage for this system of which very faint traces of the former ridges and furrows are just about detectable.

Because the irrigation channels are most often constructed within a curve of the river it is normal to find that a road or footpath crossing the valley floor will bridge both the river and one or more of the artificial watercourses. Thus just below **Coombe Bissett** a track fords the river at **113262** and, as a footpath continues northwards to Homington Down crossing a number of channels. It is the case that man made watercourses are generally straight, natural ones more wayward. However long disuse often means that carriers have fused into drains as a single stream; sometimes the origins can be teased out by using the early maps.

The Ebble continues on the south side of the valley, past extensive meadows to the next road crossing at **Homington (125262)**. As often at road crossings the valley floor has narrowed to little more than two hundred metres. The river is crossed by a narrow humpback bridge. Immediately below this the river takes water from a main drain alongside the right hand side of the road, over which, without any intervening hedge, there is a good view of the downstream meadows. This drain has emerged from under a single arched, mainly brick, bridge on the far side of the narrow valley floor just before the road curves right and climbs steeply towards Homington Down. In common with many such 'secondary' bridges the overgrown trees and bushes, sometimes even in winter, can make it very difficult to work out how the watercourse actually fits in to the scanty remains of a system.

The situation is somewhat clearer at **Odstock (148262)**. From Odstock Hospital on Britford Down a long descent to the 'secondary' bridge over what is clearly a main carriage at the northern edge of the valley floor. Between here and the two arch stone bridge over the river the downstream meadows are clearly visible. Some isolateed stone structures and hatch abutments in the river can be seen. Some five hundred metres downstream, near to the church and accessible from the road **(151262)**, is a small landscaped area with a bench seat, reached by crossing a disused set of hatches. These formerly created the head of water in the river to feed the clearly visible main carriage watering the meadows past Longford Farm to Nunton Bridge. Here is possibly the most accessible example of the irrigation control system on the Ebble.

NADDER VALLEY

This second of Salisbury's five rivers rises near Donhead St Andrew and flows roughly north to Tisbury then generally east to Wilton, where it absorbs the Wylye and on to Salisbury where it is in turn absorbed by the Hampshire Avon. Areas of most interest for the purposes of this chapter are between Tisbury and Salisbury where the valley has widened. Most of the crossings bridge more than one watercourse which helps to identify the very broad outline of a system. The meadows on the valley floors are generally easy to see, the ridge and furrow pattern in places reasonably clear. On the less 'improved' areas the line of each disused watercourse tends to be marked by various of the many coarse grasses and sedges, distinctively taller and often corn coloured. These are attracted to the wetter areas indicating that the former carriers and drains (particularly the latter) remain naturally damp. Because the irrigation systems no longer function the watercourses, often flooded in winter, do not actually dry out properly as they would formerly have done before sheep could be brought on.

A minor road runs south from the village of **Dinton to Fovant (009037)** crossing the principal valley road (B3089), and then the railway line beside the former station. Continuing across the valley floor (at a contour height of about

69 metres) the road, Catherine Ford Lane, bridges three separate watercourses. Some 250m beyond the railway, the first is an early three arch stone structure bridging a well watered main carriage that has left the river near a footbridge about 300m up stream. This is likely now to have 'short circuited' to a tail drain lower down and thence back to the river. It will have been feeding much of the system downstream from the crossing on the north side of the river. Much of the general ground pattern can be seen. Although systems may be long disused it is not uncommon for the main irrigation watercourses to remain in use as part of the natural river flow, as here. Even if this is not the case they often fill naturally during wetter parts of the year.

From the modern two and half inch map it appears obvious that the named **'Catherine Ford Bridge'(009307)** is the central, relatively modern, single span concrete and stone structure over the main river and the contiguous parish boundary. There is then a third, southernmost, quite substantial concrete and brick bridge over a dried up watercouse. The bridge seems excessive for what appears likely to have been a tail drain for the system this side of the river. It is this structure that has a plaque recording that it is the Catherine Ford Bridge rebuilt by Wiltshire County Council in 1938. There is, no doubt, an explanation for this apparent anomaly. Possibly the construction of the nearby now 'Dismantled Railway' had some impact; it is not marked on the 1901 map and its construction (and dismantling) in the twentieth century might have had some effect on the watercourses.

However another significant factor is introduced by looking at the same 1901 Ordnance Survey 1:2,500 map (sheet 65.11) This shows that the apparent 'tail drain' has been carried over the river by an aqueduct about 500m upstream having apparently drained meadows to the north of the river and then become the main carriage for lower meadows on the south side. This would account for the stature of the bridge identified (or misidentified) by Wiltshire County Council as Catherine Ford Bridge.

The river crossing aqueduct here is the only one found in this study although a syphon under the Nadder at Harnham is shown on early maps. However aqueducts are not unusual within individual systems where a carrier may be taken over a drain. For example there are at least three on the Harnham meadows. Nor is it unusual for a tail drain to be recycled as a main carriage but normally on the same side of the valley. The river, particularly as here with the parish boundary, usually separates ownership or occupancy. This may not have been so in this case. Crucially none of this becomes apparent without going back to the 1901 map although the absence of any more detail even then suggests the system had been disused from a fairly early part of the nineteenth century. The existence of former irrigation is, though, clearly apparent from the vegetation pattern and the faint traces of ridge and furrow on the meadows still to be seen.

Some three kilometres downstream is the road route from **Baverstock to Compton Chamberlayne (035310)** where the three arch stone bridge at Horse Shoe Bridge crosses the river. Of greater archaeological interest are the 'hidden' remnants of a further watercourse south of the river. Looking downstream from the bridge a small mound can be seen a few metres into the field on the right (Figure 3.5). Pushing aside an August crop of nettles to reveal the top of the stone arch, it becomes apparent that this is a buried culvert, the near end collapsed and the other arched end just visible above the silted bed of a watercourse. It is on the line of a shallow depression indicating a former irrigation channel, probably a tail drain. It is not uncommon to find such tail drains close alongside a river, collecting water from the drains at right angles to it.

This depression, projected back through the buried stone structure to the road disappears into a tangle of undergrowth. On the upstream side of the road a piece of white wooden rail gives the clue for a watercourse. From the river bank there is a good view of the early three arched stone bridge. But it takes careful scrutiny, and luck to spot among the undergrowth a disused ditch and the further stone arch taking it into the (no doubt blocked) culvert under the road. There is no indication of any of this on the 1901 map suggesting, again, that this system has been disused for probably at least a century and a half.

The road continues towards Compton Chamberlayne but before turning to climb the valley side has a junction with the alternative crossing by what is formally classified as footpath to **Dinton Mill (025312)** where the river swings to the north side of the valley. Some 100m along what is actually a cart track it reaches a stone arched bridge without parapets over a dry main carriage. This formerly watered the large area within this loop of the river. Just in the field to the right there is ample evidence in the form of mainly collapsed stone or concrete hatches or conduits.

At **Barford St. Martin (058312)** the main A30 road crosses the valley, raised on a causeway and offers an unusual view, from a height (and, despite the heavy traffic, from safe pavements), of the meadows in both directions. Many of the irrigation patterns can be picked out, particularly upstream to the left where silted drains become wide and wet near the river.

South Burcombe (072309) provides again the pattern of bridging the three watercourses. From the village almost immediately there is a two arch brick and stone bridge with a good flow of water closely followed by the seven arch mainly stone structure crossing the river. The piers on the latter have semi-circular rather than the more normal triangular water breaks. These two watercourses are linked a few yards upstream by a diagonal channel, again with a good flow, crossed by a footbridge with five narrow apertures. All this seems too much to relate to a tail drain from the narrow strip of valley floor on the south side and may just reflect the natural formation of the river.

The main area of irrigation to the north of the river, the residual pattern reasonably clear, fed into the tail drain that runs alongside the left side of the road and enters the river beside its bridge. This has some flow of water and presumably reflects natural land drainage. Just before the road begins to climb steeply the third bridge over the former main carrier would be inconspicuous were it not for a very modern repair on the right side indicating continued use for land drainage and road run off.

The Nadder absorbs the River Wylye some 300 metres downstream from the two bridges on the A3094 where the rivers emerge from Wilton Park, and from where irrigation systems resume, although all long out of active use. There are two further accessible and interesting footpath crossings before reaching Salisbury, Broken Bridges and Town Path. The latter is very fully dealt with in Chapter 4. The name Broken Bridges does not appear on any modern map but is well known locally and refers to the crossing between **Bemerton and West Harnham (126303)**. It offers a fair amount of visible archaeological evidence, has good views of the meadows, retains some bucolic feel, is well used and provides some idea of how many valley crossings must have looked in the past.

From the road at Bemerton the path edges round some twentieth century buildings (they post date the 1901 revision of the 1876 Ordnance Survey survey) crossing two strongly flowing watercourses in quick succession - the river and a tail drain - with parallel modern vehicle bridges. It almost immediately then bridges a substantial weir with two large stone apertures; the adjacent building is shown in 1901 and the combination suggests that this was a mill leat and race. There are then three further watercourses, normally dry unless flooded in winter. These are now crossed by modern concrete slabs, each on early stone abutments that are likely originally to have carried plank bridging: maybe the eponymous 'broken bridges' after the irrigation system had decayed and before concrete replacements were needed for more demanding pedestrians going about their business? The first of this series has, embedded in the watercouse at the edge of the bridge, two iron stanchions serving no discernible purpose. The third crosses a three aperture hatch with clear paddles grooves in the well preserved stone. These hatches will have controlled a section of the main carriage, its onward course now marked by a line of willows.

The path continues, over one further slab bridge, for about 400m, generally on a low unmade and often muddy causeway, a normally dry and overgrown tail drain on the right and a tree screen marking the line of the river some 150m to the left. The abandoned irrigation and characteristic vegetation patterns of long disused floated meadows are clearly to be seen on both sides until the path reaches a substantial, flowing tail drain. This carries normal land drainage but formerly gathered water from extensive systems upstream and now has a recent single span wood and steel arched bridge. Under the centre of the arch is a rather lonely looking redundant stone pier from a previous two span version and on which a scratched '1923' can just be made out.

The valley crossing then immediately turns sharply left on to a more obvious causeway above the flood prone ground on either side. On the left is overgrown woodland concealing the river until just before the path joins Upper Street in West Harnham. To the right is a trackway, known at inclosure in 1783 as Long Hills Lane, well used in preference to the overgrown path, and then a further tail drain from the former meadow system (now normally ploughed) stretching for a kilometre or so across to the main road. Much of this former system on part of the natural flood plain has been build over, necessitating in recent years a flood protection bund – and an undated 'NRA Flood Defence' plaque. Finally the footpath crosses the standard concrete slab to bridge the tail drain which then continues alongside Middle Street and eventually rejoins the river beside the Harnham Mill at the end of the Town Path - the next crossing.

The final crossing of the Nadder valley before it becomes the Avon is the so called Town Path linking Harnham to Salisbury: more precisely from **West Harnham to Fisherton** over two separate arms **(136294 and 138298)**. This is dealt with in much greater detail then any of the crossings above in Chapter 4.

WYLYE VALLEY

The River Wylye shares its name with the village of Wylye mid way along its course. It rises south of Maiden Bradley near the western edge of Wiltshire and in its upper reaches has the alternative name of Deverill. It curves north for some miles dropping from some 150 to 110 metres just south of Warminster, the downs rising in places very steeply to between two and three hundred metres. From here the valley widens and falls less steeply, generally south-east, to Wilton where it is absorbed by the Nadder.

The four kilometres of minor road from **Sutton End to Sutton Veny** drops gently for a short distance, crosses the river at **Jobs Mill (873432)** and then immediately climbs steeply to the wooded downs. The crossing actually links settlements, as is normal, but at some distance from both: at the mill the river has swung towards and is tucked under the steeper side of the valley. Approaching across the narrow valley bottom there appears to be no trace of a main carriage but a drain by the left (downstream) side of the road, and the telltale coarse vegetation indicates former irrigation. To the right improved meadow gives way to coarser just below the single arch mainly brick bridge over the river. The former mill is on the further bank, the weir visible up stream. The line of the outflow from the mill is beneath the modern garden (with the only example of a croquet lawn seen in this study) and reappears from under the left of the road to rejoin the river in a conventional way some 200m downstream.

The river now takes a northerly curve of twelve kilometres or more past Warminster and through Heytesbury. There is little accessible visual evidence of the impact on the irrigation systems of the mid nineteenth century railway or the late twentieth century A36 (T) Warminster by-pass. Nor is there any obvious evidence from the map of disruption apart from apparently existing watercourses being accommodated by bridges or culverts. South east from Heytesbury there are five marked footbridge crossings before the next road between **Upton Lovell and Corton at Suffers Bridge (943402)**. Here the river, now on the 85 metres contour is tight under the steep southern side of the valley and the route continues as a modern bridleway and former drove snaking up 100 or so metres of the steep convex slope to the downs; the highest point here a marked 187m on the Wessex Ridgeway.

From Upton Lovell the minor road runs south, under the railway, and then along, not across the valley. The map shows an artificial watercourse, possibly the main carriage, immediately alongside on the right. The river runs parallel some 500m away and the two are shown joining, together with an intervening drain, at the bridge. On the ground these are manifested by three separate bridges, two over watercourses in decay. A few metres downstream, there is a classic start to a floated system. The river turns quite sharply left through a large disused hatch (now bridged by a cart track) while a main carriage continues straight on and over what would have been hatches but is now a fixed weir. Some 600m further downstream the long disused system becomes rather less classic when the main carriage short circuits into a tail drain and rejoins the river.

Judging, again from the modern map, building the **causewayed A303 (T) (006380)** across the Wylye Valley had a major impact on whatever disused systems remained on either side of the river. This applies particularly to the major grade separated junctions with the two valleys roads: the developed A36 (T) and the minor road from Stockton to Wylye. However from here down to Wilton they run neatly together, rarely much more than 500m apart on the valley terraces. From both sides there are good views of the valley floor, the river and other watercourses are often screened by tree lines and undergrowth that would not have suited earlier occupants. Their overriding concerns were grass, grazing and hay.

There is the residue of some apparently complex systems upstream from the single road bridge connecting **Hanging Langford and Steeple Langford (037371)**. These can be explored by the footpath crossing some 500m upstream and from the path, part of a community project, also upstream from the bridge. This walk bridges the river via a former hatch just before it joins with a major drain from the system upstream, to create a pool much favoured for swimming by local children. There is a small information board.

Below the bridge any former floated systems for nearly a kilometre, and the width of the valley floor, long ago gave way to what is now the Wiltshire Wildlife Trust's Langford Lakes reserve. Not former watercress beds, as so often in such situations, but gravel pits acquired by the Trust in 2001 and promoted as a 'premier place to see wetland birds and habitat restoration in action'. Indeed, a very good, possibly the best site at which to appreciate most aspects of a Wessex chalk valley. But not the historic irrigation systems and their archaeology, for which go to the systems at Harnham or Standlynch, both dealt in detail in Chapter 2. Similarly a little further down the Wylye the meadows above the crossing from **Stoford to Great Wishford (084355)** are fully described in Chapter 2.

At the site of the former Wilton railway station on the northern edge of the town the line from London and Salisbury splits. Both lines cross the Wylye on causeways built in the late 1850s probably across systems still in active operation, each line crossing two major watercourses and a mass of smaller carriers and drains. From the modern two and half inch map some deduction can be made about what accommodation was needed, in particular a few instances of watercourses clearly distorted alongside a causeway. Little is accessible or easily seen except perhaps to the very well informed and quick-eyed observer on a train. Curiously, the best published source of information is the end paper map in A G Street's book about Ditchampton Farm (Street 1946). Easier to see are the causeways into Salisbury from the east, the line from London across the Avon meadows (now in the Central Car Park) and the line from Southampton across the Bourne at Milford.

Wilton is the junction of the River Wylye with the Nadder. Several watercourses from each valley thread their way through the town and the rivers finally unite (as the Nadder) just below Wilton House Park. Both are bridged, within less than 200m, by the A3094 crossing from **Quidhampton to Netherhampton (107308)** each on its respective valley terrace, just above the flood plain. To confuse the issue there are actually three bridges because the Wylye splits into two for a short distance as it leaves the park. Some hatches are visible just downstream but the actual junction of the rivers (110308) is out of sight.

AVON VALLEY

The name 'Avon' associated with a waterway is used in three different contexts in Wiltshire. A River Avon rises in the north of the county and flows westward to the sea beyond Bristol. The Kennet and Avon Canal, connects the River Kennet at Reading with the (Bristol) Avon at Bath. Quite separate and further south than either of these is a second River Avon. This flows south to the sea at Christchurch, much of it through Hampshire, and tends therefore to be known as the Hampshire Avon. This work however limits itself to Wiltshire.

The river rises above Pewsey. Two floated systems on the narrow headwaters are described in Chapter 2 and from Pewsey down to Upavon there is scanty evidence of some similar small systems. Below Upavon the river becomes stronger, the valley wider and the sides steeper as it slices through Salisbury Plain. Ordnance Survey Explorer 1:25000 sheets 143, 130 and 131 spread out side by side provide a dramatic sense of the emptiness of the plain. Early writers who ventured to cross it commented on its loneliness: nothing to be seen except the odd shepherd - and the vast flocks of sheep. Settlements are confined to two north south routes, the eastern one following the course of the Avon and most of them providing a valley crossing in the usual way. There is map evidence of irrigation for most of the stretch to Durrington and Amesbury.

a

b

d

c

BRIDGES

a

b

c

d

3:3

MEADOWS

a

b

c

d

a

b

c

d

STRUCTURES

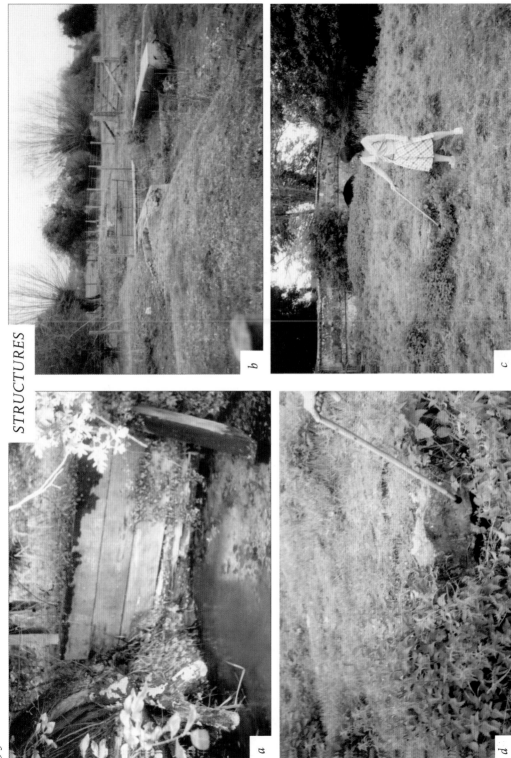

a

b

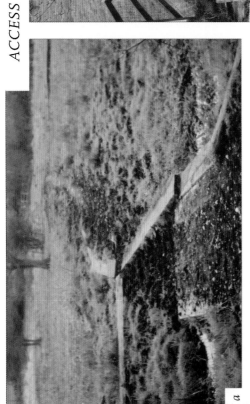

d

c

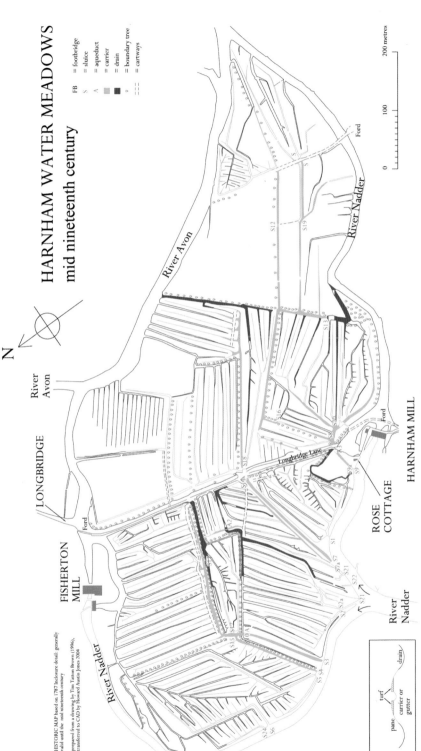

HARNHAM WATER MEADOWS
mid nineteenth century

N

River Avon

River Avon

LONGBRIDGE

Ford

FISHERTON MILL

River Nadder

River Nadder

ROSE COTTAGE

HARNHAM MILL

Longbridge Lane

Ford

Ford

River Nadder

FB   = footbridge
S   = sluice
∧   = aqueduct
▪   = carrier
■   = drain
○   = boundary tree
‡‡‡   = cartways

0   100   200 metres

pane   turf   drain
carrier or gutter

HISTORIC MAP based on 1787 Inclosure detail: generally valid until the mid nineteenth century

prepared from a drawing by Tim Tatton Brown (1996), transferred to CAD by Howard Austin Jones 2004

4.1a Harnham water meadows as they were in the mid-19th century, with only slight changes to the irrigation system shown on the 1787 inclosure map. Four significant changes have since taken place: south-eastern ford replaced by bridge c. 1860; means to water north-east meads (Longbridge, Deanery, Rowlas, Hussey's, Parsonage) blocked off by mid-20th century; demolition of Fisherton Mills c. 1960 and creation of 'Fisherton Island' from the north-western sliver of meadows for housing; restoration of irrigation systems started 1989 and continues. This map prepared from a drawing by Tim Tatton Brown (1996), transferred to CAD by Howard Austin Jones (2004).

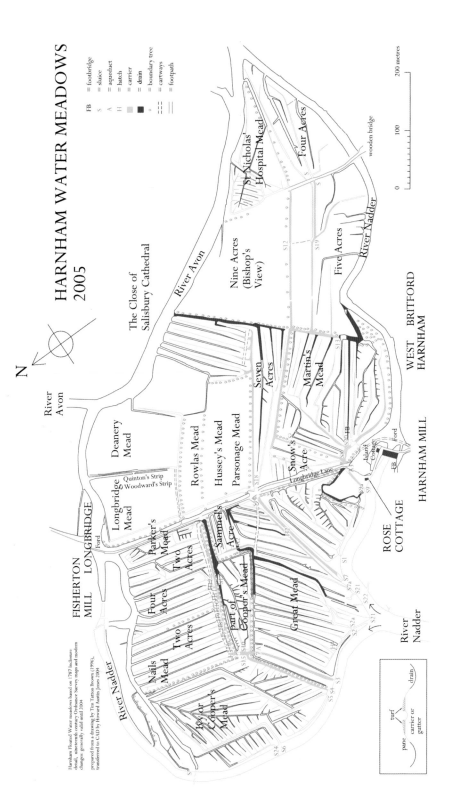

HARNHAM WATER MEADOWS
2005

N

Harnham Floated Water meadows based on 1787 Inclosure
detail, nineteenth century Ordnance Survey maps and modern
changes: generally valid until 2004

prepared from a drawing by Tim Tatton Brown (1996),
transferred to CAD by Howard Austin Jones 2004

FB = footbridge
S = sluice
A = aqueduct
H = hatch
▪ = carrier
■ = drain
• = boundary tree
⋮⋮⋮ = cartways
— = footpath

River Avon

FISHERTON
MILL   LONGBRIDGE

River Nadder

The Close of Salisbury Cathedral

River Avon

Deanery
Mead

Longbridge
Mead

Quinton's Strip
Woodward's Strip

Ford

Longbridge
Mead

Parker's
Mead

Two
Acres

Four
Acres

Two
Acres

Nails
Mead

Ivy or
Cooper's
Mead

Rowlas Mead

Hussey's Mead

Parsonage Mead

Sammel's
Acre

part of
Cooper's Mead

Seven
Acres

Snow's
Acre

Martin's
Mead

Nine Acres
(Bishop's
View)

St Nicholas'
Hospital Mead

Four Acres

Five Acres

River Nadder

Great Mead

Longbridge Lane

Adam
Cottage

FB

FB

Ford

ROSE
COTTAGE

HARNHAM MILL

WEST   BRITFORD

HARNHAM

wooden bridge

River Nadder

S12

S19

S18

S13

S8

S9a

S9

S1

S7

S21

S22

S2

S2a

S21

S5

S4

S3

S15

S10

S24

S6

0   100   200 metres

pane
turf
carrier or
gutter
drain

4.1b Composite map of the West Harnham system as at 2005 with modern sluice (or hatch) numbers used by the managing trust.

DROWNING

a

b

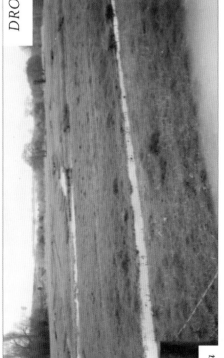

d

c

MID-NINETEENTH CENTURY AQUEDUCTS & HARNHAM MILL

4.6a

4.6b

4.8a

4.8b

4.8c

3.1   RIVERS

a Landscaped area by a disused triple hatch on the Ebble (151262), accessible by a footbridge from the road near Odstock Church.

b The largest set of hatches encountered in this work (107308) with 14 apertures, on the Nadder below Wilton Park and just above its confluence with the Wylye. The hatch paddles have been removed and the piers carry the footbridge over a weir with a fixed drop of a metre or so. The view is downstream from the parapet of the bridge on the A3094. For the moderately courageous the structure can be seen from the road bridge.

c random example of bridging a minor watercourse in the Wylye valley; probably a main carriage or a tail drain. The typical overgrown banks make these difficult to spot although the white guide railings are an almost infallible guide.

d unusual iron hatches at Stratford Bridge on the Avon (13 0329): the river at this point is on about the 50m contour line at a narrow pinch point in the floor in a much wider valley. Behind the camera the downs rises very steeply to Old Sarum iron age hill fort (122m) while across the valley there is a gentle rise to the far side on Bemerton Down, 102m at its highest. (A measured drawing of this feature is in Chapter 5).

3.2   BRIDGES

a Milford Bridge (157298), last bridge but one on the Bourne, looking upstream and said (VCH) to have been rebuilt c.1386. The two left hand semi-circular arches shown, with an intervening pointed cutwater and moulded string course below the parapet, bridge the actual river.

b The two right hand arches of Milford Bridge, pointed but otherwise similar, cross the mill tail. A narrow 14th-century bridge does not take kindly to modern traffic, hence the traffic lights just visible, top right. A research assistant volunteered beyond the call of duty to get these shots.

c A kilometre further south the Bourne is bridged (155292) by the modern A36 Southampton Road at Dairyhouse Bridge. The road is reached between two tiny fragments of green flanking superstore warehouses.

d Emerging on the south side of the main road the Bourne flows on for some three hundred undignified metres to join the still rather rural Avon behind the superstore car park.

3.3   MEADOWS

a Neglected meadow on the Bourne with characteristic coarse vegetation marking the disused carriers and drains; the main watercourse is maintained and the hatch being pointed out is newly repaired.

b Meadow at Harnham on the Nadder, regularly grazed by sheep but not restored to working order; the main carrier is on the left, parallel carriers and drains running from left to right. At bottom left a mid-nineteenth century concrete pipe drain is the first of series forming a cartway. In the distance, upper left, is a copse, alien to the meadows, but recently planted as part of the modern environmental programme.

c A well grazed meadow on the upper Nadder, the residual lines of water channels still marked by the slightly corrugated appearance of the ground. The hedge line, bottom, marks the valley crossing road; the river line at right angles to it is top right, shown by mature trees and fresh vegetation, with a further grazed meadow on the far side.

d Typical meadow on the Avon at Lower Woodford, from the valley road, and normally grazed by cattle. A remaining channel from the disused system appears to be used to drain road run-off water. Centre left is a footbridge across the main carrier for the Woodford system (see Chapter 2) and beyond it the wooden weir controlling the river. From this viewpoint the river, downstream from the weir, is lower and invisible behind the line of the main carriage. Just beyond the river the far side of the valley has a shallow rise across pasture and then steeper ploughed land toward Salterton Down (rising to 100 m).

3.4   HATCHES

a Standlynch Mill on the Avon. The near end of the building is the disused mill (formerly generating electricity) with a modernised dwelling beyond. The first of the five sets of hatches in this complex (see Figure 2.16) is in the foreground, nine apertures in all, six dismantled and three working behind the wooden 'balcony'. These hatches control the main carriage towards Downton on this side of the valley. Just beyond the pontoon the leat feeds the mill race apertures. The trackway turns right and becomes a footpath, past an eel house and a further set of hatches to the modern steel nine aperture weir crossing the river.

b Detail of hatches at Standlynch; old ironwork is secured to the timber cross beams by modern steel bolts.

c Haxton Weir (147491) on the Avon, with wooden hatches in an iron frame. The viewpoint is over the race apertures to the adjoining former mill, out of shot on the right. The nearest weir aperture has no wooden paddle and thus permanently open; the remaining three can be operated from the footbridge which the rather firm notice suggests leads to nowhere.

d The reverse view of Haxton Weir; metal matting reinforcement a commonplace safety measure on wooden footbridges and, top left, evidence of the mill's latest use as a brewery.

3.5 STRUCTURES

a A 'drop board' device of indeterminate purpose on the Bourne. This seems to be a somewhat informal structure, the horizontal boards held only by light upright timbers; there are no stone or concrete piers and it is typical of many ad hoc solutions to be found.

b Mid-nineteenth century concrete aqueduct (listed as A1) at Harnham on the Nadder. A main carriage from the river flows from bottom right towards top left, crossing an inverse siphon piped drain, the concrete lined entrance and exit of which can be seen to left and right. The carriage can be controlled by drop boards, of which one is in place; slightly further on an old iron gate propped below the sheep fence is a pragmatic way of stopping animals using the dry carriage bed to seek greener grass.

c A grass covered mound on a Nadder meadow with a hint of stonework.

d Some nettle bashing with the author's walking stick by a quite unsuitably clad research assistant reveals the arch of a small bridge. Further prodding might reveal a hatch; either way it is a clue from which a start can be made, by walking the area and with help of an old map, to work out the configuration of the system. Ideally such a structure should be consolidated as suggested in the example of stabilizing a brick aqueduct in Figure 1.7.

3.6 ACCESS

a Narrow valley floor of the Avon headwater at the Jones's Mill reserve showing that public access can be a mixed blessing although damage is mitigated by the Wildlife Trust's board walks.

b The Town Path bisecting the meadows of the Harnham Water Meadows Trust on the Nadder at Salisbury where residents and visitors can readily appreciate the meadows without direct access. The spillway hatch on the left is vulnerable and has been vandalised; litter is a never ending problem.

c Motorists, or at least their passengers, can appreciate the Britford meadows from the A36 near Salisbury. Only those on foot are likely to spot the hatch house across the valley, to be picked out in the photograph at the base of the tree line and just to the right of the lamp post.

d Longford Castle Park from the Bodenham river road (170259). No meadows and no access here but three watercourses detailed in Figure 2.15. Between the

two trees on the near bank the confluence of the Ebble (left) and the Avon is visible; the river continues downstream to the right as the Avon. Upstream on the Avon. out of sight, a weir creates the head of water for Snow's 1665 main carriage towards Standlynch. The spillway from this is the third watercourse (extreme right) obscured by branches.

4.5 DROWNING

a Some of the Harnham meadows have not been restored to a point where channels can deliberately be filled, or drowned; these drains on the western meadows fill naturally after very heavy rain.

b An unrestored tail drain carries rainwater to a culvert under the viewpoint on the Town Path but the flow is impeded by vegetation further along and causes the water to back up in the channel.

c This main carrier (also shown in Figure 2.12 from a more restricted angle) has been restored and carries water (see Figure 4.1) to distributor channels further across this meadow. Sheep will not cross the water filled channels and historically would not have been put on the meadows when they were; however in the short time between this photograph and that in 2.12 being taken the llama moved from standing in the distance to resting in the foreground by jumping the intervening channel.

d Main carriers on the eastern meadows, regularly watered from Sluice 18; the distant sheep a perennial attraction.

4.6 MID-NINETEENTH CENTURY AQUEDUCTS

a The concrete structure shown in figure 3.5b, marked A1 on the map, from a different direction, the carriage from the right crossing the drain which apparently, given the ground levels, syphons water under it; the drain continues along a modern fence line to a further, iron, aqueduct, A2, pictured below.

b Roles, and size have been reversed; a narrow carrier feeding only a small area crosses what has become a major tail drain; roughly the mid points of four centuries are represented here – seventeenth, the meadow; eighteenth, Fisherton Mill House; nineteenth, iron structure; twentieth, author.

4.8 HARNHAM MILL

a In 2004, from the northern end of the ford, sloping down to the left.

b In 1832 (Hall 1834) with a new warehouse and showing Island Cottage (c 1780).

c In 2004 from the south side of the ford.

However the first crossing is far from usual. The Army has used the open expanse of the plain as a training area since the late nineteenth century and nowadays has designated crossings on the few roads and along the river, specially reinforced for heavy armoured vehicles. At an otherwise indeterminate point about halfway between Upavon and West Chisenbury the modern map shows **Tank Crossing (134540)**, from nowhere to nowhere which is no doubt how tanks like it. The meadow on the right bank upstream has all the features of disused irrigation and standing close to the river bank in the residual depression of a seventeenth or eighteenth century former drain a massive single span iron girder bridge on concrete piers is framed by woodland on each bank. On the straight track approaching the bridge from each side of the valley fierce signs enjoin a maximum weight of eighty tons, speed of 6 limit miles an hours and one vehicle at a time.

There are several further such crossings between here and Durrington to enable units to become 'non-tactical' while moving between the manoeuvre areas of the eastern and central parts of the Plain, or vice versa. However there is a concentration of military installations and housing at **Netheravon (150485)**, none of it visible from the bridge. This has very long, low modern concrete parapets which conceal the crossing of three separate watercourses very close to each other. How they relate to each other is unclear from both the map and tree screened banks. Among the trees on the right below the bridge a small watercourse joins the river at right angles; and can soon be followed along the side of the meadow next to the road. It is not, as may at first be supposed, a tail drain from upstream which has crossed the road under a further bridge but can be followed as a roadside stream through the village and traced to a spring across the main road on the valley side.

The main interest lies in the construction of the middle section. The modern bridge has been built over a substantial seven aperture stone hatch. The piers extend some way out from the bridge itself, clearly visible by looking over the downstream parapet. From the river bank upstream, the apertures can be seen as nothing like the downstream piers, apparently of concrete with a ribbed surface. There is no sign of any hatch plates or machinery which would be on this side of the bridge. Presumably the road is much wider than the original hatch so the apertures had to be extended.

Below Amesbury is the stretch usually known as the Woodford Valley after the villages of Upper, Middle and Lower Woodford. Before reaching these the river curves to the west at Wilsford-cum-Lake, site of the 'bog body' (McKinley

2003) referred to in Chapter 1. From here it runs more strongly, winding from side to side of the valley, creating a number of classic systems exemplified by that at Lower Woodford, described in detail in Chapter 2.

The systems in the immediate vicinity of Salisbury originally continued almost into the city, as is still the case with the Nadder at Harnham. Nowadays the physical evidence is diminished and some of the area near to the city has long been built over. The first crossing of relevance is at **Stratford sub Castle (128330)** to the east of the valley. The road from the village and the steep road down from Old Sarum converge at a bridge, the first and most substantial of three across the valley. To a casual glance, driving past, it seems obvious that the first bridge is over the river. However a closer look reveals a stone hatch of eight narrow apertures very close to the upstream parapet: and just upstream of the far end of the bridge a further stone hatch with two wide apertures, against a farmtrack bridge.

The apparently main watercourse is now the main carriage, the eight aperture hatch providing fine tuning to the irrigation of the meadow systems between here and Salisbury; and of course in its original role only carrying water for the few months when meadows were intermittently drowned. The actual river swings sharply right through the cruder two-aperture weir which was used to create the necessary head of water. The river then runs very slightly backwards alongside the road for 100 metres or so and turns sharply left under the near arch of the second, three arched stone bridge (not readily visible below mundane modern brick parapets). The other two arches take the flow from another watercourse of uncertain status; possibly a tail drain but a hatch visible upstream suggests otherwise. A plaque records that this is Avon Bridge widened by Wiltshire County Council in 1936. This identification is confirmed on the modern map and the first bridge referred to as Stratford Bridge. The third unobtrusive bridge crosses a drain.

An industrial archaeology oddity and undoubtedly the most interesting aspect of this crossing is that the hatch paddles above Stratford Bridge are made of iron rather than wood (Figure 3.1d). The conventional rack and pinion lifting mechanism is cast or forged in the usual way, the latter mounted normally on a wooden beam .However the pinion cog wheel is set very close to the iron plate and at right angles to the toothed bar of the rack; the pinion spindle thus at right angles to the hatch plate. Much ironwork to be found on the meadows identifies a manufacturer, sometimes with a date but nothing is immediately visible here.

Some two and half kilometres downstream the river passes through the Avon Valley Local Nature Reserve (an SSSI). The information boards identify a water meadow and a withy bed on the right hand side, both suitably ecologically overgrown. Below this a gentle double bend takes it past a main carriage hatch on the right at a point identified on the modern 1:10,000 map as **Black Well (138309)**; past the Leisure Centre on the left then the supermarket complex on the right. Now on the Salisbury city side of the valley, it passes under Ashley Road to an almost straight stretch of nearly a kilometre between Castle Street and the Central Car Park, past Town Mill to the bridge joining **Salisbury to Fisherton Anger (142300)**.

Naish's map of Salisbury, first published in 1716 shows 'meads' almost as far as Fisherton Street. He identifies Blew Bore Mead on the site of the modern coach station and signs 'Way to the Meadows' from a point now occupied by Fisherton Street railway bridge. These irrigated meadows, in operation by 1716 are likely to have been created at least by the late seventeenth century. The valley is wide and shallow at this point, the floor some 50 metres above sea level. The meadows played their part in the sheep corn cycle by providing for the flocks from the grazing and arable lands of Bemerton Down (reaching 100m) and Bishop Down (110m) a distance of some 2.5 kilometres apart. Proximity to the city with its stables and dairies also meant a local market for some of the hay crop. This situation prevailed until the middle of the nineteenth century after which, apart from the widespread pattern of systems beginning to fall into disuse, the 'green finger' was steadily eroded by commercial activity creeping north from Fisherton Street.

The first impact was from the railway. The London and South Western Railway Company's line from London finally made its connection to the existing Fisherton Station in 1859, crossing the valley by a kilometre or so of causeway. This must have been an awesome sight to anyone looking up the otherwise empty valley. It respects the irrigation watercourses, crossing them by two major bridges and a tunnel. The first bridge, a single arch, crosses the river and walkers along the riverbank can admire its curved brickwork. The second has three arches of similar design; two still in use for the access road between the ring road and central carpark, the third closed off and unused. Why three arches is unclear. As late as the 1:10,000 map of 1961 they are shown giving access northwards only to an area marked with the sign for swampy ground, in other words derelict watermeadow. The south portal of the tunnel on the other side of the carpark (marked on the 1901 map as 'Subway') cannot easily be seen behind the waterside vegetation but the northern end can. From St.Paul's Road it is possible to see through the 100m length of a fine tall narrow structure taking the Black Well channel diagonally under the former eastern goods yard.

The invasion continued with the Market House Railway built by 1859 and extensive malthouses in the early 1860s. Finally some time after 1929 the cattle market moved from the Marketplace to the area Naish showed as Blew Bore Mead but still leaving some area of disused irrigation south of the railway. By 1973 the cattle market had moved to the other side of the railway, in due course to be replaced by the present supermarket and its car park. The remainder of the area up to the river is now taken up by some housing, the fire station and open amenity space.

Tracing the development of the watercourses starts with Naish's 1716 map on which two are shown flowing parallel from the top centre. The eastern one, nearest to the city, is drawn very firmly with straight man made artificial sides, in the same way as the Avon Navigation is delineated down the left of his map. This is clearly the straight stretch recognisable today and often regarded as the River Avon. It is in fact, for most of its course, the leat for Town Mill: Naish also shows how it fed the city's street 'canals' The other is less clear. It is allowed to meander slightly, indicating the river, its lower stage coinciding with the modern watercourse towards and then along Water Lane to the Nadder near Long Bridge. His explanatory panel fills the space that might show a third watercourse from the Black Well sluice.

This sluice can be seen, little changed, with a footbridge over a substantial stone structure, two four foot wide wooden paddles, iron work and a broken stone bed (Figure 5.7). The watercourse it controls flows southwards, under Ashley Road, between the supermarket and gasholder and then under the ring road and the truncated St Paul's road. It emerges briefly before plunging into the splendid 'subway' tunnel to the Central Car Park. At this point the 1901 map shows it feeding a complex of carriers for, probably, a disused system and the water being picked up into a tail drain, under Fisherton Street and along Water Lane eventually to the Nadder by the Long Bridge. It later became a single watercourse and the final alignment was altered to the present layout in Queen Elizabeth Gardens.

The river continues along the S bend, picking up a ward boundary, to a point just beyond the present Ashley Road and level with the end of the supermarket. Here the river formerly split from the mill leat by means of a substantial sluice, much the same size and style as Black Well. The 1901 map shows the river, identified by the ward boundary (which at one point leaves a short canalised section and shows the previous natural line) meandering towards, under and beyond the railway, past the end of the mill to the millpond and under Fisherton Street - the original westward exit from the city and despite many more since, our designated valley crossing point.

At some time between 1961 and 1973 the river line was changed. The sluice is still there but its flow much reduced by the use of two small apertures instead of the former hatch plates. A small channel disappears under the supermarket and emerges at the other end into the Black Well watercourse. Just below the railway a small hatch feeding a minor meadow carrier has been developed into a major powered sluice, a single steel plate allowing a drop of some two metres across a width of 3 metres. The alignment of the banks immediately above this sluice leaves no doubt that this is the point where the mill leat continues straight on and the rivers follows its own course to below the mill just above Fisherton Bridge. Naish in 1716 shows the leat providing power for two mills.

At the site of the first, some 100m upstream from the second, a solid modern sluice feeds a short steep and narrow channel, formerly the mill race and then until the 1930s Salisbury's outdoor swimming pool. The second mill still stands, described as 'former mill, the E part brick, probably of c1756, the W part medievalizing (sic), c1898' (Pevsner). Looking upstream from Fisherton Street two sets of three apertures can be seen. The smaller right hand set must have powered the original machinery while the later creation of the electricity works needed the power of the larger. The massive machinery can be seen from upstream in the middle of a parade of shops. Three 1m wide races create a drop of perhaps 1.5m controlled by screw operated metal plates. The cross beams are substantial timber baulks, nine inches square, and bearing rectangular metal plates marked 'Armfield'.

Below the mill the race and river meet to flow under the Fisherton Street bridge. Naish, in 1716 shows this as a footbridge; the residual lines of its associated ford appear to be detectable in the building lines on both upstream sides and the slope from the city side. For some two hundred metres a somewhat canalized course has in recent years been softened by the creation of 'artifical natural' banks to improve the habitat. Below Crane Street bridge (with, again, its ford line detectable) the Avon skirts the Cathedral Close. It is joined by the arms of the Nadder from the two sides of Harnham meadows and continues to Ayleswade Bridge, Bishop Bingham's 1244 improvement to the southern exit from Salisbury; and where this survey of the Avon ends.

BOURNE VALLEY

A bourn (without a final e) is defined as a small stream, especially one that runs periodically from springs in the chalk. A 'winterbourne' is commonly regarded as a stream limited to winter flow. However Wiltshire usage (D and G 1991 quoting Davis 1794) offers a 'valley between chalk hills; a river in such a valley; also river and valley jointly'. Both seem to suit the River Bourne. This rises near Burbage, just south of the Kennet and Avon Canal and some six kilometres east of the Avon at Pewsey. It flows south to join the Avon below Salisbury, a point to point distance of some 35km, the actual watercourse perhaps some 50km. On the face of it a supply of water limited to winter should not inhibit the creation of an irrigation system which has to be dried out from March to September anyway. Useful studies of the hydrology of the river and effect of floods are Delair 1991 and 1997.

However on the upper reaches of the Bourne there is very little map evidence of floating until **Tidworth (235484)**, where much is likely to have been obliterated by the military town. Much lower down, although the names of Winterbourne Gunner, Winterbourne Dauntsey and Winterbourne Earls suggest periodic flow, there are modest indications of floating and the river seems eventually to flow happily into the Avon behind a supermarket car park the year round.

In between, some eight kilometres south of Tidworth at **Newton Tony (217406)** the newly reconstructed bridge, a single concrete span and wooden rail parapets, crossed a completely dry river bed in late October 2004. At **Allington (205394)** the river also runs along the village street and was equally dry. If it was as dry at this time of year in previous centuries it is not surprising that there is no evidence of irrigation in this part of the valley. Some 300m upstream from **Idmiston (196376)** – still at October 2004 – the water has returned – presumably from springs. Here a small two arched stone access bridge has a paved bed with a slight drop at its lower end and may in the past have contained hatches.

The unmade lane connecting **East and West Gomeldon** crosses two watercourses, the first a ford **(181369)** which has every appearance of being the river but probably is not. Just upstream from the footbridge beside the ford is an unusual hatch with two unequal apertures. The left hand one is some 1.5 metres wide with an iron hatch plate suspended from an iron bridge by two vertical rack arms raised or lowered by two pinions mounted on the usual square section spindle above the bridge. The plate can only be lowered to the level of a stone sill with a drop of no more than a metre. In contrast the right hand aperture is only about 0.5m wide with a single iron plate controlled by a conventional setting plate and claw and providing a drop of nearly two metres to an eel trap above a paved stone bed.

The configuration of this structure and the long straight watercourse leading to it strongly suggests a mill and its leat. The map shows the river meandering away to the western side of the narrow valley floor, crossing the lane further along. Where it parts company with the leat is uncertain but it may be where, on the ground, there is now a single (iron) hatch about 150m upstream, dropping to a watercourse enlarged as a fishing pool. 'The supposed site of the Gomeldon Mill' was excavated and the report, published in 1968 (Musty), describes it in detail and a small number of finds, but was unable to confirm the existence of a structure. The mill recorded in 1518, and possibly 1821 remained classified as 'lost'. The same article identifies eleven mills between Newton Tony and Mumworth (at the mouth of the Bourne, see later) those at Ford and Milford still in existence, nine lost.

The lane continues, bridging the river, and just before joining the main road, the main carrier to the system downstream. This lane has long been superseded by road crossings up and down stream at Porton and Winterbourne Gunner. In appearance it must be much as many crossings were before developing into made roads with bridges. (Figure 000).

In contrast some five or six kilometres downstream where the shallow valley widens out between **Bishopdown and Laverstock Down (158310)** there is possibly the newest bridge crossing the Bourne. This carries a footpath and cycleway intended primarily for the pupils living on the estates covering much of Bishopdown safely to Laverstock's several secondary schools. Up and down stream the meadows show clear signs of former irrigation. Just a kilometre or so downstream the downs on either side close in on a narrow neck of valley crossed by a bridge built to carry a major route east from Salisbury some six centuries earlier, in existence by 1400.

At **Milford (157298)** the 1901 map shows a complex of main watercourses but the whole valley from the bridge down to the Avon is marked 'Liable to Flooding'. Looking upstream from the narrow bridge (not the safest thing to do) the river flows in from the left and by means of two right angle turns runs under the bridge joining the outflow from the mill race in a wide pool. A main carriage formerly left the mill leat above the mill, crossed the river by means of an aqueduct and then turned south under the road. This, and the river then flowed close to each other and shared a bridge when they had the railway causeway built above them. The carriage eventually reached the Southampton Road at Muttons Bridge, the river at Dairyhouse Bridge.

Both these bridges are on the final Bourne crossing from **St Martins to Petersfinger (155292)**. Naish's map of 1716 shows the start of this route out of Salisbury from behind St Martin's and marked 'Road to Southampton and Romsey' – which it still is. Initially there is a steep descent from the extreme end of the Bishopdown Ridge (the modern Tollgate Road) to the valley floor and flood plain, as modern motorists can sometimes attest. The name Muttons Bridge may conceivably derive from Mumworth, one of the cluster of hamlets predating Salisbury near St. Martins and recorded in a 16th-century perambulation as 'Moniworthe, where sumtyme was a mill'. Similarly Dairyhouse Bridge crossing the river some 200m further on has an eponymous ring. Habitation here was possible (Rose Cottage on the Harnham Meadows is an example) but must have been precarious.

Neither Muttons nor Dairyhouse Bridges are marked on the modern Explorer map and, unless on foot, are easily missed. From the bottom of Tollgate Road the former is some 300m along the Southampton Road (say 155293). The main carriage is piped under a superstore car park and the main road before emerging beside a motor tyre repair business as a small watercourse with a modest flow (Jan 05). A remnant of Mutton's Bridge itself remains in an early stone parapet over two rebuilt modern brick arched channels. Some 50m further along the road the River Bourne is crossed by Dairyhouse Bridge. Upstream the river is squeezed between a superstore to the west and, on the other bank, a car spares yard and an electricity substation. A narrow road to the left and alongside both is the earlier main route to Milford. Beyond the substation (or from the very back of the carpark on the west bank) the river is visible with some derelict open space. This is the last surviving fragment of the watermeadows at this end of another of Salisbury's 'green fingers'. Further along past a caravan settlement, the road becomes a footpath through the tunnel under the railway, beyond which the lower Milford meadows can be seen.

Immediately below Dairy House Bridge the Bourne turns sharply left to run parallel to the road as far as the corner of the superstore car park. Here it turns sharp right to join the Avon. The 1901 map shows a similar course but the final right map turn is into a main carrier providing water to a comprehensively detailed system stretching some six or seven hundred metres between the road and the Avon to just beyond the modern sewage works. That main carriage has at some stage fused, or being encouraged to fuse, with a tail drain into the single water course that is now the river.

The natural river line, shown in 1901, is back under Hatch's Bridge (at the present Tesco roundabout) alongside the road, finally returning under Petersfinger bridge towards the Avon. The line is still quite clear, marked by the strip of overgrown land between the road and Tesco carpark. This route across the mouth of a Winterbourne valley was no doubt generally passable, at least for the medieval traffic between Salisbury and Southampton, serving the wool trade. Early maps (Ogilby 1675; Andrews and Dury 1773) show the route crossing several water courses, perhaps with a ford and the raised footway as remains the case on the Avon at Harnham Town Path. In due course it was turnpiked and remains, a step too far one might think, as the irritating congested A36 (T).

CIRCUIT

In focusing very closely on the floated or irrigated systems on the valley floors an important aspect of the sheep/corn cycle can be overlooked. The 'added value' created by investing heavily in irrigation was only delivered at one remove via bigger flocks and their impact on the cornfields. The acreage of irrigation is only a tiny proportion of that devoted to downland grazing and arable. The sheep were put on the watermeadows for part of each day for no more than three months of the year. The previous sections of this chapter have illustrated features of each river valley in linear sequence. To demonstrate the contrast this section sets out a circular route starting and finishing at Ayleswade Bridge crossing the Nadder at Harnham.

This circuit of some thirty kilometres can be followed on Ordnance Survey, 1:25,000 Sheet 130 (South). It starts by crossing **Ayleswade Bridge (143291)** southwards, turning right past the Rose and Crown Hotel where the valley side begins to rise, crossing the modern road and continuing up the increasingly steep Old Blandford Road. Joining the modern A354 the route crosses the downs for some four kilometres before dropping to the Ebble valley at **Coombe Bissett (109265)**. A right turn up the Ebble takes the circuit to a Bishopstone junction **(085266)** and again, turning right, to the next long slow climb to Hunt's Down and Hare Warren. From here there is a steady descent to the Nadder after a downland crossing of some five kilometres. Very shortly after this the Wylye is also crossed because here, at **Wilton (102313)**, the two valleys merge.

From the valley floor, the route climbs The Avenue (a former grand approach to Wilton House, now better known for the army headquarters and a local 'park and ride' transfer point) to **Camp Hill (125m, 113335)**. A steep, winding descent – the hallmarks of a former drove route – then reaches the Avon valley after a crossing of some three kilometres. Turning right, down the valley brings the journey to **Stratford Bridge (129329)**. From here the next downland crossing is some fourteen kilometres via the Laverstock Down crossroads **(143333)** near Old Sarum, and the Portway to **Ford (170343)** in the Bourne Valley. Then the A338 and A30 close the circuit, down the Bourne Valley, back to Salisbury and Ayleswade Bridge.

4
Town Path

INTRODUCTION

The terms sluice, hatch, and weir are variously defined but essentially all mean much the same thing; they describe a device for controlling a flow of water. Davis at the beginning of the nineteenth century used 'hatch' for all the control structures on floated water meadows. The Ordnance Survey later in the century used 'sluice'. In this work generally the convention has been to use 'weir' where there is a change of river level; to follow Davis with 'main hatch' for where water is taken from the river into an irrigated system; and use 'hatch' for any controlling device within it.

However the Town Path is part of the Harnham system and local management convention has been followed. Most structures are called sluices except for the very smallest on pipe bridges. The mead (or meadow) names and the sluice and other numbers referred to in this chapter will be found on Figure 4.1 (in colour section). Hatches of all sorts are described in a more general way in Chapter 5. The term 'cartway' has been adopted as the generic term for the various ways intended for wheeled vehicles. It is defined as 'a rough road on a farm' which seems to fit.

This has no doubt been a crossing of the Avon from Fisherton Anger to West Harnham, two hamlets predating the creation of New Sarum, since time immemorial. It remains - some 750m – the unmade Longbridge Lane making the crossing through two fords; the footpath alongside, Town Path, raised on a causeway at some stage, built up and given a hard surface. This crossing is selected for detailed description because it is a very well used pedestrian route, easily accessible for visitors, bisects the 88 acres of floated meadows managed by an environmental trust, and from which just about every aspect of floating and drowning can be illustrated. Its position is shown Figure 2.11, one of the systems described in Chapter 2, and on the 1787 inclosure map at Figure 1.6. By the late nineteenth century maps show Longbridge Lane, a cart-track from the ford below Fisherton Mill to the ford below Harnham Mill; and the Town Path as a footpath on its causeway alongside. A 1931 sale document (Thake and Taunton) refers to the 'historical old water road'. Even if the name Longbridge Lane has fallen into disuse, both path and lane remain unchanged, now formally classified as a Footpath and a Bridleway. The street name sign at the Harnham end says 'Town Path'.

However this relatively small area, between two arms of the River Nadder, is only the remaining part of formerly much more extensive systems stretching upstream on both sides of the river, now mostly built over. The 'island' nature of this system, accessible only by three fords, a mill halfway along each side and fragmented ownership meant both that its irrigation system was unusual and that it will probably have provided only hay crops and not early grazing for sheep. The isolation also meant protection from development and survival as a 'green finger' into the centre of the city, unlike the Avon finger above Fisherton, discussed in the previous chapter. The meadows and their irrigation systems are described largely as they can be seen from Town Path, mainly from three vantage points – Long Bridge at the Salisbury (or Fisherton) end, by the so called Reservoir at the mid point, and from near Rose Cottage just before Harnham Mill at the far end.

There is no known documentary evidence of when the Harnham meadows were floated. The somewhat tangled relationship of some of the watercourses may suggest that fragmented ownership and occupancy meant different parts at different times. Almost certainly the process will have been started by the mid-seventeenth century and completed well before inclosure in 1787. Chronological development that can be established is outlined in a short history published by the Friends of the Harnham Water Meadows Trust (Steele and Tatton-Brown, undated but after 1989). For study on the ground now there are five useful sources – the 1787 West Harnham Inclosure Map; late nineteenth century Ordnance Survey 1:2500 maps; 1931 sale document for Fisherton Mill and its estate (Thake and Taunton); 1949 and 2000 aerial photographs; and post Second World War large scale maps.

BACKGROUND

At this point it is useful to remember a number of general distinctions between how an observer in earlier centuries would have seen meadows (any meadows, not just those here) and how this particular type of landscape looks today. The irrigated water meadows were much emptier of trees, shrubs and fences; sheep were only grazed on the meadows for a few weeks early in each year; and for much of the year the watercourses were deliberately dried out.

The meadows were originally common fields uncluttered by boundaries and to some extent this may have changed with inclosure. But it did not necessarily mean a single change at a particular date and an Inclosure Award and its attendant map may record what already exists (Sandell 1971). This appears to be the case for the Manor of West Harnham where some of the irrigation channels regarded as of seventeenth century construction clearly relate to specific blocks and strips named in the 1787 Award (Figure 1.6). There were, too, constructional changes made in the mid nineteenth century reflecting changes in ownership.

The sheep now seen grazing for much of the year on the meadows managed by the Harnham Water Meadows Trust (accompanied in recent years by a llama) are misleading as far as the historic practice is concerned, for three reasons. In the heyday of floated water meadows the animal was the Wiltshire Horn, nowadays a rare breed (and see Chapter 5). As part of the sheep/corn cycle the flocks grazed the water meadows only from mid March until the initial hay crop had been eaten off, perhaps six to eight weeks. Moreover, as far as the Trust's meadows on their 'island' are concerned, it is highly unlikely that sheep will have been grazed at all (although the normal practice will have prevailed elsewhere within the manor).

Sheep and water do not readily mix and flocks will not have been driven twice a day through any of the three fords providing access. One was replaced by St. Nicolas's Bridge to the southern end of the 'island' in the later nineteenth century. Rebuilt in recent years this remains a light bridge, used by the grazier to deliver and collect his stock; hence the modern situation. However the problem of sheep and water has not entirely gone away. In one area a riverside fence has had to be put up where some apparently tasty herbage attracts the animals to the river's edge. The odd one falls in, drowns, or if spotted in time has to be rescued (with difficulty – a sodden sheep is heavy). Historically on these particular meadows the real value must have been the hay crops, possibly two a year, made more profitable by being very close to the city with a host of hungry horses; a survey for military billeting in 1686 (Chandler 1991) shows 'accommodation for' 998 horses.

Historically the irrigation systems will only have been activated for relatively short periods in the autumn and winter (see Chapter 1 and the fuller description of the annual cycle in Annex 2). In particular the watercourses had to be empty when sheep were to be grazed in order to get them on to and about the meadows at all. On many meadow systems watercourses may today be seen with water all the year round because they have become a natural part of the river drainage; typically a former main carriage will join up with a tail drain providing a diversion channel, sometimes as an overflow, for the river. Many examples have been quoted elsewhere in this work, usually describing the watercourses as having 'fused' or 'short-circuited'.

LONG BRIDGE

The bridge itself (138298) is first illustrated by the painter John Constable in his *Salisbury Cathedral from the Meadows* painted in 1829 (Figure 4.2). His viewpoint was a few metres back from the bridge on the left bank of the Nadder to give the cathedral and the famous rainbow pride of place. Although it took some time in the completing this painting was initially produced on the ground. Constable was famously accurate and for this study the foreground is much more important than the nominal subject. From the left an empty waggon is drawn into the ford and the footbridge appears in the bottom right corner. At bottom centre a dog stands beside a path on the timber revetted bridge abutment. Only part of the narrow plank bridge itself, with a single handrail, is shown; perhaps a quarter of its total length. The painting shows three apertures between vertical wooden supports and part of a fourth. Making a judgment (helped by the size of the dog) it may be that this was a flat plank bridge with six to eight supports.

However the first documentary evidence is more that a century earlier. It is shown on Naish's 1716 map of Salisbury as an unnamed footbridge, continuing as a footpath marked 'to West Harnham'. The name is sometimes said to derive from an early owner of Fisherton Mill called Long: maybe so, maybe myth. But the name appears elsewhere (near Stinsford on the Frome for example, and Longbridge Deverill on the Wylye) and another more likely explanation is simply

4.2 *Ford at the northern end of the Town Path downstream from Long Bridge.* Salisbury Cathedral from the Meadows *by John Constable painted in 1829 (top) and a similar scene photographed in 2004 (bottom). The bus is drawn by Hamish and Walter.*

that it was longer than the usual plank bridge over a small watercourse. Naish shows it with a central support.

It has been suggested (by Christopher Taylor) that the bridge is not actually especially long and that the name originally meant the complete length of the path with all its bridges. There are examples of this in other parts of the country. It is shown on the inclosure map, without elaboration and leading to Longbridge Lane. Constable painted the 1829 rickety looking structure described above. Although it was no doubt repaired or rebuilt many times a photograph with boys clustered on it in 1907 (Daniels 1988, 136) looks not dissimilar, still flat but with two low handrails, just tidied up with sawn timber. A distant view in 1931 (Thake and Taunton; see Figure 4.3) shows it unchanged. Miss Foster (Foster 2003 and Annex 1) refers to a flat planked structure in about 1950. The present single curved wooden span from the 1980s is clearly of the modern safety conscious era: the sides are shoulder high.

4.3 *Long Bridge (centred, middle distance) seen from the drawing room window of the mill house in 1931 (photograph copied from a sale catalogue).*

From the bridge looking north towards Fisherton and Salisbury an unmade track enters the ford. Until the former Bowling Green Nursery was transformed into the present landscaped Queen Elizabeth Gardens in the 1950s the track was also the course of what is sometimes known as the 'back Avon' - in fact the 'short circuited' carriage and tail drain carrying water from Black Well hatch above Fisherton, discussed in Chapter 3. Of course until perhaps late in the nineteenth century while the meadows below Black Well were still being operated the watercourses, including this one, were actually dried out for a good part of the year. Naish shows it crossed by a footbridge and, by implication a ford giving access to the mill. The present channel, normally with some water, flows through the gardens to a point some 150m downstream from Long Bridge, popular for safe paddling in summer. Some 300m downstream is the confluence of the Nadder with the Avon and it is the latter that then borders the meadows until it meets the other arm of the Nadder at the southern tip of the 'island'.

From where his easel was set up, Constable's view of the cathedral is now obscured by trees and the modern observer has to be on the bridge. The waggon in the foreground is, as might be expected, of the distinctive and elegant Wiltshire style drawn by three horses in line. What were known in Wiltshire dialect (D and G 1991) as the 'raves' over the front wheels and the 'waggon-hoops' over the rear, extending the load carrying capacity, are somewhat more exaggerated than some of the modern standard illustrations (Vince 1970). The inclusion of the waggon is of course part of the artistic composition of the picture. Nonetheless it shows what must have been a frequent sight at certain times of the year – a waggon going to the meadows to collect hay, although as there are no 'hay ladders' fitted at the back and front it might be that the horses are just being watered. This is one reason for the modern horse drawn bus to include the ford (Figure 4.2) in its circuit round Salisbury during summer months, when much is made of the Constable connection.

Looking upstream the view is dominated by Fisherton Mill House described variously as Queen Anne (Thake and Taunton), mid eighteenth century (RCHM) and 'late C18th probably' (Pevsner). The Freehold Water Corn Mill, described at the sale of the mill and its estate in 1931 (Thake and Taunton) as a four story building of 'massive brick construction' (Figure 4.4) with two turbine hatches, was demolished by 1969 as were several smaller buildings up stream also fully described in the 1931 sale. They included a second 'Ancient Barley Mill' mill, used 'years ago . . . in Woollen manufacture' (that is as a fulling mill). At that date it had two sluice hatches, an eel stage with two hatches, an eel pound and an old water wheel and housing. The eel catch was a 'valuable perquisite...estimated to yield about £40 per annum'. Most watermills appear to have had an eel trap or stage but any sort of context such as this seems to be rare. The mills have been replaced by two modern weirs. Eels have almost completely disappeared from local rivers, according to a recent short piece in the Wiltshire Wildlife Trust's newsletter.

Looking south from the bridge is Town Path on its causeway, classified as a Footpath right of way, and a watercourse immediately on its left, now classified

4.4 *Fisherton Mill from Long Bridge in 1931; the four-storey mill on the right was demolished about 1959 but the house remains.*

as a Bridleway right of way (the nineteenth century Ordnance Survey term was 'Bridle Road') and formerly well known as Longbridge Lane. On either side are watermeadows.

From Long Bridge it becomes apparent why the Bridle Road, Longbridge Lane, was described as the 'historical old water road' (Thake and Taunton). In fact anything going through the ford, as illustrated by Constable, would be using what is both a road and a watercourse, the source of which will become apparent (the Nine Mile River at Bulford had the same dual function). Straight ahead on its modern surfaced causeway is the footpath, a popular walk, often very busy with competing pedestrians, dogs and cyclists. There will always have been at least a slight causeway (similar to that upstream at the Broken Bridges crossing; see Chapter 3) with flat plank bridges over the several watercourses that interrupt its length. Archaeological opinion is that under the modern rendering of the substantial built up causeway there will be at least some eighteenth century stonework. However in earlier centuries the traffic to and from the tiny hamlet of Harnham is unlikely to have justified anything very sophisticated. Henry Fawcett, the Victorian member of parliament and Postmaster General who liked to walk across the meadows was blinded in 1858. After this, according to his biographer 'he showed his usual nerve in crossing narrow planks across streams' (Stephen 1885) and the drowner had to take care that planks were in place (*Hatcher*

Review 5 quoting Stephen). Miss Foster writing of 1949 says the path was 'narrower and rougher really only the edges of the fields fenced off'.

The so called 'eastern meadows' to the left and the 'western meadows' to the right are named as they were at inclosure in 1787 on Figure 4.1 (colour section). The various blocks and strips have been progressively consolidated into three separate elements: 38 acres owned by the Dean and Chapter of Salisbury Cathedral since 1931, 50 acres by the Harnham Water Meadows Trust since 1991, and a few acres at the southern tip of the 'teardrop island' which are not discussed further. In 2002 a lease was signed with the Dean and Chapter so the Trust now manages all 88 acres as a single entity. The River Avon along the eastern side is a Site of Special Scientific Interest (SSSI) and the whole of the Trust's land is designated as an Environmentally Sensitive Area (ESA), elegible for grant aid subject to the agreement of DEFRA - the ministry responsible for agriculture and the environment. For modern day to day management purposes a limited number of mead names are used. The natural historians in their reports use numbers.

For its first 300m the path is flanked on the left by the watery lane and then Longbridge Mead with Rowlas, Hussey's, and Parsonage Meads further on, all now part of the same area; to the far left is Deanery Mead. Neither path nor lane are owned by the Trust and the maintenance of both is the responsibility of Wiltshire County Council, the highway authority. The overgrown state of the watercourse is often the subject of what archeologists on Salisbury Plain would call the 'badger in the barrow' problem. Here it is the conflicting concerns of the environment in the shape of water voles, and allowing the water to flow properly. The 'vole in the water' syndrome. Figure 4.1 shows the former extensive irrigation detail in these first eastern meadows, still visible from the air in 1949 (The Downland Partnership, undated but after 1991). Why most of it has now disappeared so thoroughly is uncertain, but as is not uncommon on 'improved' meadows, in some lights or under a dusting of snow the flattened but characteristic pattern of ridge and furrow can just be picked out. The ground is well grazed but drain lines are sometimes detectable from coarser vegetation.

To the right the first part of the western meadow was originally made up of five strips named as Parker's Mead, Two Acres, Four Acres, Two Acres and Nail's Mead, shown as separately watered from the north on the 1787 inclosure map. They were consolidated in the nineteenth century and the regular pattern of carriers and drains, parallel to the path, is watered by a carrier from the distant Sluice 3. Beyond the second tree line (Nail's Mead Copse) Cooper's Mead can be watered from restored Sluices 5, 12 and 11 and formerly from others now lost in the creation of Fisherton Island. At the south end of the five strips a cartway has been created with pipe-bridges across the carriers. Each bridge has a very small hatch at the end allowing particular carriers to be watered only as needed. The cartway provides a route for hay waggons without damaging the watercourses and was part of a redevelopment carried out by the Earl of Pembroke in the mid-nineteenth century (Steele and Tatton-Brown).

A few metres further along, the modern grazing boundary at a right angle to the path is marked by a wire sheep fence. Beyond this are the remnants of a double tree line with between them a tail drain from the small block described as 'part of Cooper's Mead'. The line of this drain also provided access to Cooper's Mead when it was in separate ownership and the access was a condition in the 1931 sale particulars. When waggons used it in summer the irrigation channels were all dry. Town Path now crosses the drain by a brick arched bridge, not really visible except for its angled abutments on the west side. Formerly there had to be wheeled access to both the mead cartway and, between the tree lines, Cooper's Mead. The Town Path has obviously been reconstructed on its present causeway for many years but a previous layout is likely to have been a removable plank bridge. This may be faintly suggested by a widening of the path to a former gate, a very slight residual dip and the curious angle of the culvert.

Finally, past the double tree line on the right is Sammel's Acre. Its four carriers and intervening drains are watered from Sluice 7a, across Great Mead and then over the iron aqueduct A2 visible some 80m from the footpath. Water from the four drains runs into a tail drain and is piped under the causeway. Nowadays Sammel's Acre is sometimes called School Mead because it is an easily visible area that can be properly 'drowned' in the historic way for demonstration purposes.

CENTRE

Past Sammel's Acre on the same side there is an end on view of the pipe drains on each carrier and drain. Further on it becomes clear that these provide a diagonal cartway across the meadow, part of the mid nineteenth century alterations. Now, about 300m from Long Bridge, a complex set of features is effectively the centre point of the total system. A brick arched bridge carries both lane and footpath over a substantial main carriage. This (supplemented by one other further along) provides water for all the eastern meadows. Looking west, this channel divides

Great Mead into two parts, the larger part to the right, or north. A clump of vegetation two hundred or so metres away marks its source at Sluice 7 on the Harnham arm of the river and the biggest sluice on this system with three apertures for wooden paddles. As a main carriage it reflects the earlier fragmented ownership of the meadows. Conventionally (compare, for example with Lower Woodford illustrated in Chapter 2) a main carriage of this size would run nearly the complete length of a system with a series of control structures so that different parts could be drowned in succession.

Here its crosses the western Great Mead without interruption to supply about half the acreage of the eastern meadows. The northern part of Great Mead is supplied by three single aperture sluices; Sluice 7a, part of the same stone structure as Sluice 7, and Sluices 2 and 2a some 6om away across the point of the island and a little distance on the other arm of the Nadder toward Fisherton. Back on the Harnham arm the south side of Great Mead is supplied by single aperture Sluices 1 and 9a. This south side also has the diagonal cartway over pipe drains. In this general area there are also three totally ruinous sluices for which no restoration is planned; and a fourth which, given the irrigation configuration, should exist and is regarded as lost, completely buried but possibly recoverable.

Still looking west, immediately beside the pathway is the single aperture Sluice 14 (Figure 4.7). The nomenclature follows the conventions adopted by the local management but this structure could also be described as a hatch with a single wooden panel. This is a spillway that can be used to release surplus water from the main carriage; raising the paddle allows water to flow along the stone channel beside the path, under the causeway and back to the river without having been used for irrigation. The Drowner, in operating the system, needed to control flow and levels at various points and this is one of the devices he could use.

Looking the other way from the bridge the nearest feature is a large hexagonal stone basin, often referred to locally as the 'whirlpool' but actually a reservoir providing the Drowner with another way of fine tuning the water supply to different parts of the system. There were originally four outlets. Just about detectable to a sharp archaeological eye, on the left wall is the outline of an aperture that contained a sluice to supply the systems, now lost, to the north: Parsonage Mead, Hussey's Mead, Rowlas Mead, Longbridge Mead and Deanery Mead. Straight ahead is the single aperture Sluice 18 (Figure 4.7) through which the main carriage continues, to water Seven Acres and possibly Nine Acres. This

4.7a   The Town Path running north from the spillway at sluice 14

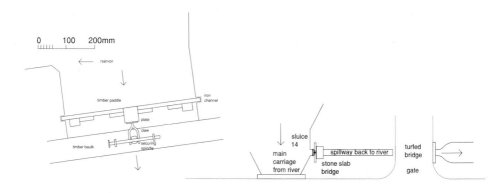

4.7b   Spillway and reservoir complex at Town Path mid point (right) and enlarged detail of sluice 18 (above)

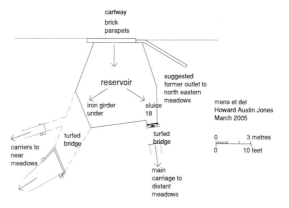

last is sometimes called Bishop's View and from it is the reverse view of the South Canonry, now the residence of the Bishop of Salisbury. Finally on the far right corner a grassed footbridge crosses two apparently uncontrolled carriages, the first supplying part of Martin's Mead, the other Snow's Acre. Visible about 150m along the main carriage is a modern wooden bridge made, in common with three others on the western meadows, of high quality material designed for a life of at least a century. This is a part of the restoration programme and is intended to allow vehicles and plant to cross watercourses without damage and to move sheep when channels are full.

ROSE COTTAGE

Continuing along the causeway, the accompanying sunken cartway is normally dry although there is, towards the end, a pipe drain for any overflow from Great Mead. To the right the diagonal carriers in the lower part of Great Mead lose their water eventually to one tail drain parallel to Town Path and another around the boundary of the wooded Rose Cottage garden visible just ahead. On the left, Snow's Acre is screened by a well grown hedge line but becomes visible on reaching two bridges shortly before Rose Cottage, the ford and Harnham Mill.

At this point the footpath crosses the main carriage from the double hatch Sluice 9 which feeds part of Snow's Acre and Martin's Mead. This sluice can clearly be seen at the end of the main carriage through the cottage garden (Figure 4.9). Where it is bridged by the footpath the channel also provides a bridge over the end of the tail drain by which water that has irrigated the southern part of Great Mead is returned to the river at its now lower level below the weir. This three level structure (Figure 5.2) has been heavily restored at various times but by peering closely through any undergrowth the early stone arch at the lowest level can be seen. Evidence of the most recent work are initials scratched into the southern wall of the carriage just below the footbridge.

The cartway crosses the main carriage by a recently rebuilt brick bridge and from the end of its slope down to the river makes a wide sweep round Harnham Mill to ford the southern arm of the River Nadder. The footpath continues, raised well above the mill pond, alongside the garden and then the front of Rose Cottage, left across the modern weir and around the front of Harnham Mill. At the end of the ford the two ways are reunited as a surfaced road for 100m or so to a junction with the minor road through West Harnham.

4.9 *Main carriage through the garden of Rose Cottage. The cottage is Harnham Water Meadows Trust's base on the meadows for its management, information and educational work. Interested young students think it is never too early to study irrigation!*

Rose Cottage is thought originally to have housed the Drowner who would have controlled the adjacent weir and the irrigation on some or all of the meadows. It is equally likely that Island Cottage, beside the mill on the opposite bank, had a similar purpose. Both cottages were remote from the hamlet, on the very edge of the valley terrace. Island Cottage is described as extensively altered and 'perhaps of late 18th-century origin' (RCHM building 589). It is the older of the two dwellings and the only one shown on the 1787 Inclosure Award Map. Rose Cottage, now with Grade 2 Listed status, is dated c1840 (RCHM building 590). Life at Rose Cottage during the second half of the twentieth century is evocatively described by Miss Jane Foster who lived there for some fifty years until her death in 2004 (Foster 2003 and Annex 1 in this work). The cottage has very recently been bought by the Harnham Water Meadows Trust for use as a visitor information and education centre and to house a warden.

Harnham Mill and its weir, together with the weirs that have replaced the former Fisherton Mill, provide the barriers on the river that create a head of water with sufficient energy to drive a flow across the full extent of the meadows. There had to be co-ordination of the competing needs of milling and irrigation but the nature of this competition is sometimes overstated. The meadows were drowned for only short periods; for example 'some meadows that will require the water for three weeks in October, and the two following months, will not perhaps bear it a week in February or March, and sometimes scarely two days in April and May' (Davis). The river has dropped from its historic level in recent years and, despite, the restoration of most sluices and much of the surviving system of irrigation channels, drowning at will is no longer a modern option although some major channels can be kept partly full.

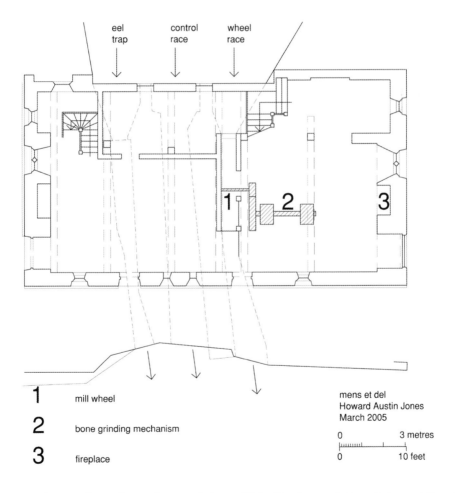

1   mill wheel

2   bone grinding mechanism

3   fireplace

4.10 Harnham Mill: amalgam of a ground plan published by the Royal Commission on Historic Monuments and one from a contract document of 1879 when the bone crushing machinery, shown, was to be removed.

Myths abound but the full and illustrated definitive description of Harnham Mill (RCHM building 588) has it dated as *c.*1500, and suggests, given the four large fireplaces, that it had been a paper mill (documentary references to paper-makers in Harnham, however, mostly refer to activities at Bemerton Mill, which is just in West Harnham parish: *VCH Wilts* 4, 245).Later it was a fulling (or cloth) mill and a bone mill. In a single-page contract dated 25 April 1879 a James Sangar rents the eastern part of the ground floor from Henry George Gregory (privately owned document displayed in the hotel restaurant). A condition was that Sangar was to remove the 'present bone crushing machinery consisting of rollers and flywheel and stands'. He was also to 'erect partitions and doors to lock on both sides of the wooden casing of the waterwheel,' could widen a door at the back and could install a copper [a cooking or laundry boiler] 'under the present chimney breast'. This had to be removed at the end of the tenancy together with other 'trade fixings'. There is a plan of the ground floor and the bone crushing devices, incorporated in Figure 4.10. Until, probably, the 1920s the building was used to create tallow; at least one elderly resident remembers the smell!

It is now a restaurant and the adjoining early nineteenth century warehouse a hotel. From upstream three wide arches can be seen from the hotel garden. These apertures, described as the head race, wheel race and eel trap, narrow to their drops under the building. The wheel race, and the drop, can be seen from inside the restaurant. The three outlets are visible from downstream beyond the ford. On the far corner of the hotel two streams joining the river are tail drains, the residue of extensive irrigation systems further up the south side of the Nadder. Part of this remains as an open space in Middle Street, West Harnham. Similarly an open space off Lower Street, along the river below the mill may have been part of the next system on this side of the river. It now offers a playing field and a cricket pitch. Where it adjoins the ford families picnic, and children swim in summer. At both ends of the Town Path, at both fords, indulged ducks flourish!

5
Means

Improved corn output on the Wessex chalkland from the early seventeenth century needed (somewhat crudely to summarize) three things to operate the sheep/corn cycle. These are dealt with here in separate sections – sheep, water control, and the tools to do the job.

SHEEP

The iconic breed that dominated Wiltshire in the seventeenth and eighteenth centuries, and into the nineteenth, was the Wiltshire Horn sheep, quite distinctive in appearance and characterised by both sexes having horns. Those of the female are curved backwards and slightly down. Those of the male are bigger, curling backwards in the same way but with a further forward and upwards curl. These animals are barely to be seen now in the county. There are a few in small specialist flocks but the most easily found are the realistic and taxidermic example at Lackham Museum or the somewhat less realistic replica in Salisbury High Street. The latter, of indeterminate gender, is slung in an uncomfortable looking way above a religious book shop by the Cathedral Gate. It appears in photographs from 1955 but local information is that it dates from the 1930s when, painted gold, it adorned a wool shop called The Golden Fleece. If so, it was an odd choice. This traditional horned Wiltshire sheep is now promoted by its breed society as The Woolless Meat Sheep.

The breed society's history (Thwaites) provides a useful chrological survey and a lead to other sources, in particular the work of E H Lane Poole who 'during the 1950s investigated the origin of these sheep in their native country and who

5.1 Wiltshire Horn sheep: (above) A Wiltshire Ram, published to illustrate Thomas Davis's report on the agriculture of Wiltshire in 1813; (below) Modern shearling (once shorn) ewe, reproduced from Sheep Husbandry and Diseases *by Fraser and Stamp (1968).*

presented a treatise to the Wiltshire Archaeological Society'. This treatise cannot be traced either in *WANHM* (the society's journal) or its Library but what it no doubt contained is hidden away in a local work about Damerham and Martin written before 1961 and published posthumously (Lane Poole 1976). Martin is on the headwater of the (Hampshire) Allen River (which joins the Avon south of Fordingbridge) and was part of Wiltshire until 1895. Lane Poole cites the early archaeological work of General Pitt Rivers on Cranborne Chase to note that the prehistoric animal stood only four or five centimetres shorter than its modern successor, and was outnumbered by oxen and horses.

Using a wide range of published and manuscript sources, including manorial rolls still (then) in private possession, he provides details of local practice and stocking rates from as early as a Glastonbury Abbey survey of 1198. This listed a flock of 617 breeding ewes on Bustard Down but there should have been a thousand and then another flock of 500. Lane Poole probably offers the definitive local study but there are other less well sourced contributions. These included a 1979 survey of the breeds that developed from the pre-Roman Soay to the twentieth century cross (K Ponting), and a useful 1926 estimate of gross sheep numbers in Wiltshire from the mid nineteenth century (Hony). His figures were 809,000 in 1869 diminishing by decade to 259,000 in 1925, but of course no longer the Wiltshire Horn by that period.

Despite now being billed as 'woolless', during the breed's most prolific period in the seventeenth and eighteenth centuries the wool had some value, although not much, and some were no doubt eaten as well. But its success was due to totally different characteristics. A contemporary writer, used extensively in this work (Davis) observes that of the purposes for which sheep in the district were kept.

> The first and principal of these is undoubtedly the dung of the sheep-fold, and the second is the wool. The improvement of the carcase was not heretofore thought a primary object, and perhaps is in so degree incompatible with the great object of this district, viz. the hardiness of the animal, necessary to enable it to get its food on a close fed pasture; to walk two or three miles for that food, and carry its dung the same distance back to the fold; and the breeding [of] lambs was looked upon as a necessary consequence, rather than a primary cause of keeping such [a] flock.

The Wiltshire population of the county's eponymous breed was quoted by Aubrey at the end of the seventeenth century as between a thousand and two thousand on each tithing. In 1724 Defoe wrote about flocks of three to five thousand. About 1830 Cobbett apparently met a single flock of 4,000, but perhaps by then they were not the horned breed. None offers explanation of how they arrived at these figures. As ever it is Davis, who in 1813, in a serious report to the government, having ridden to all parts of the county and spoken to farmers who knew what stock they held, wrote

> The number of sheep kept in this district cannot be exactly ascertained; but from the best information that can be collected, it appears that the number of lambs bred yearly is at least 150,000, and that the whole summer stock of sheep, including lambs, is very little, if any, short of 500,000.

But the number had declined by many thousands in the previous fifty years and, 'on the down part of the district where the sheep fold is indispensably necessary to the production of corn, a diminution of the sheep stock is a serious evil'. He goes on to explain that change was taking place and he is not entirely happy with the breeding developments. The Wiltshire Horn was becoming less suited for its purpose. However during the course of the nineteenth century, changes in agriculture, artificial fertilizers and imported corn reduced and eventually removed the historic need for sheep as self propelled dung providers. The Wiltshire Horn, limited to this purpose, was no longer wanted.

They appear to have faded from the scene quickly. An early twentieth century writer (Hudson 1910, reprinted 1979) can assert, without quoting any specific evidence, that

> A solitary flock of the old Wiltshire sheep existed in the county as late as 1840, but the breed has now so entirely disappeared from the county that you find many shepherds who have never heard of it

For a more contemporary claim he quotes a personal encounter ' not many days ago' in 1910 or possibly a year or so earlier with a shepherd who knew nothing of the old breed. When Hudson told him he said it explained a puzzle. An old well that in former times had been used to water sheep had been cleaned out a few years before when

> a vast store of rams' horns was discovered and bought out, and it was a mystery to the farmer and the men how so large a number of sheep's horns had been got together; for rams are few and do not die often, and here there were hundreds of horns he understood it now because, for if all the sheep, ewes as rams, were horned in the old breed, a collection like this might easily have been made.

A memory effectively lost to those working in 1910 might well take the total decline, at least in Wiltshire, back well towards the 1840s.

Hudson's former claim, citing no source, may be borne out by an (equally unsourced) reference in the modern breed society's history (Thwaites). A dramatic coloured illustration of a ram and ewe is captioned

> The Old Wiltshire Horned Breed as seen by Professor David Low when making his illustrations of the various breeds of domestic animals in 1841. The animals depicted were bred by Mr Turner of Hindon, Wiltshire on an estate bequeathed and held on the condition that it maintained a flock of pure Old Wiltshire.

A G Street who farmed at Wilton, in later life became a well known writer on both real and lightly disguised fictional farming matters in south Wiltshire. His work covers the period he knew, from the 1870s until after the Second World War. There are mentions of water meadows but sheep barely feature at all. Nonetheless there were sheep around in abundance in some areas even if not the horned breed. These were identified in the early 1930s by an experienced local journalist, 'Peter Gurney' (who wrote about the life of shepherds, their dogs and their work on Salisbury Plain for the North Wiltshire Herald) as 'mainly flocks of Hampshires, Oxfords and Dorset Downs' (Smith 1985). They were farmed mainly for meat, were still folded at night to improve land needed later for cash crops but had little need of the water meadows. These were used to produce hay and graze cattle, the irrigation structures disused and only maintained to prevent undue flooding.

In contrast, another well known local writer, evocatively recalls one of the great sheep fairs, at Britford, near Salisbury. In *Peasant's Heritage* (Ralph Whitlock, undated but 1930s) he writes through the eyes of his father, born 1874, paying his first visit to the fair at the age of 12, thus in August 1886. Taking a flock of four hundred through Salisbury at three o'clock in the morning

> we dodged through a maze of side streets . . . having to be constantly stopping at corners to let other flocks pass. When we emerged into the wide highway of Exeter Street . . . as far as the eye could penetrate through the faintly-lit gloom were sheep. Hundreds of thousands of them in a bobbing, jostling, steaming multitude. We were more than an hour and a half traversing the mile or so between Salisbury and Britford [via the narrow Ayleswade Bridge at Harnham]. The entire length of road was packed with sheep, there being only about ten yard intervals between the flocks.

The fair was about more than just sheep and the elder Whitlock's childhood memory may have exaggerated but although sheep predominated he is unlikely, by this time, to have seen any Wiltshire Horn. They were still farmed but mostly elsewhere in the country by enthusiasts for the breed.

A meeting 'to place this valuable breed of sheep on pedigree lines' was held in Northampton on 13 January 1923. The first Flock Book of the Wiltshire or Western Horn Sheep Breeders' Association (latterly the Wiltshire Horn Sheep Society) registered 390 ewes and 157 rams in England, followed by a further 161 ewes and 55 rams in Wales, under 800 in all. The breed then flourished, 787 ewe lambs alone were registered in 1951; 812 ram lambs in 1955. This was followed by a decline and the creation of the Rare Breed Survival Trust in the early 1970s saw it classified as a 'breed needing monitoring'. In 1992 there were only 602 animals registered. The forthcoming Flock Book for 2005 is expected to show a significant increase on this.

A precise description of the breed in the twentieth century is offered by the British Sheep Breeders' Association (anon 1946 reprinted in Fraser and Stamp 1968) in a work described by its publisher as a 'classic work on sheep by a leading authority'.

> This breed, curious both in appearance and in history is somewhat similar to the Dorset Horn, but grows no wool. Most breeds of sheep have their own distinctive characteristics but without any fear of contradiction the Wiltshire Horn can claim one that is exclusively its own; it makes no pretentions of growing any wool. Its skin is composed of a thick, matted covering of hair more like that of a horse or a beast [as in oxen or cattle], with a little wool which peels as the sheep fattens. It is claimed that the absence of wool leads to greater growth of mutton, and certainly as regards maturity and weight increase of its lambs the breed is noteworthy. It has been rescued and saved from approaching extinction to play a renewed role in the spring of fat lambs, particularly from Welsh ewes in Anglesey and North Wales.

The breed society ends its history (Thwaites) with the prospect of 'pioneering a hybrid based on the Wiltshire' to produce a sheep that naturally loses its wool, requires minimum shepherding and lambs easily. This hybrid is known as the 'Easy Care' sheep! Two centuries on from Thomas Davis, whose business was improvement, he no doubt would approve.

WATER

This section is about the control of water including by watermills. However as no other type of mill is considered anywhere in this work watermills are referred to simply as mills.

Visible in the undergrowth on the upstream side of Netheravon Bridge (150485) is a damaged iron notice of the sort commonly seen on canals and railways. Enough of the wording remains to establish that it was put there by The Avon and Stour Catchment Board, which by 1958 had become The Avon and Dorset River Board (Goodland 1970), suggesting perhaps an early twentieth century date. Looking at this sign on the eastern side of Wiltshire, the River Stour which flows mainly through Dorset seems an odd partner until it is recalled that they join together just short of the sea in Christchurch Harbour. They thus realistically share the water catchment area which the Board controls. The words that can be read clearly are

> ... notice is hereby given that ... or damage to any sluice ... hatch or appliance for controlling water ... prohibited ... HG Izard [?] Clerk to the Board.

Irrigation is all about the control of water but the floated systems of the Wessex chalklands were in existence long before the nineteenth century catchment boards were established. Nonetheless, here the local board saw it as part of its role to protect the various mechanisms. They were probably by this stage just as much concerned with maintaining the structures to help with prevention of flooding to support the many watermills that still functioned rather than the irrigation systems, by then in decline.

However these declining systems had been the most advanced agricultural technique of the time when the then Earl of Pembroke and his fellow landowners saw a profitable opportunity in the early seventeenth century. Two centuries later Thomas Davis could describe the principles and practice of their creation which were still well known and used. He observes that in the formation of

> 'flowing meadows', much ... labour and system are required. The land applied to this purpose being frequently a flat morass, the first object to be considered is, how the water is to be **carried off** [his emphasis] when once brought on; and in such situations, this can seldom be achieved without throwing the land up in high ridges, with deep drains between them.

The water having irrigated an area has to drain back to the river, a recycling process repeated many times down the length of each river. The start point at each stage was to create a head of water by means of a weir or a mill, or both.

Mills

The motive power of the water meant that mills developed early. Any village that cannot claim one or more mills in its Domesday Book entry has cause to feel deprived. They long predated the arrival of irrigation in an organised way and have always had primacy with the water. For example, in 1931 at Salisbury, Fisherton Mill and its estate, including Harnham Mill (for their relative location see Figure 4.1) were sold, with the prospect of falling into separate ownership. The sale details specified that at West Harnham the 'Freehold Fulling Premises known as The Bone Mill', which had not been operated as a Mill for many years was sold

> subject to the exclusive right of the Vendor or purchaser of Fisherton Mill to the control of the Water at the Bone Mill with ingress, egress and regress to the Hatches thereon [i.e. inside the mill, controlling the three races: Figure 4.10] for the purpose of assuring the control of such water to the owner of Fisherton Mill. No riparian or water rights are included in the sale . . .

The mills, on the two arms of the River Nadder at Fisherton and Harnham were in competition for its water and it was important for the vendor at Fisherton to retain control because that mill had

> been closed for flour milling for a period of four years under the Millers' Rationalization Scheme . . . the main drives and principal elevators are retained and are available for the conversion of the Mill into a Provender Plant [dry food for beasts; fodder].

It could therefore be reactivated for some purpose other than flour milling and its water had to be protected. Elsewhere in the sale document the Mill estate was selling the 'irrigation rights' on the various meads. (Thake and Taunton).

The illustration here is that the mills 'controlled' the water and thus were principal players in creating the timetable for how water was to be shared between operating a mill and irrigating the nearby meadows. For most of the year the miller will have had a free hand. Its adjacent meadows would need their supply only intermittently between October and March, any problem presumably reduced by the greater flow during this period. In fact the drowners possibly had more difficulty in co-ordinating up and down stream. Davis, referring to the impact of the water on the grass observes that

Observations of the effects of water so brought on soon shewed him [the farmer or drowner] at what period its good properties ceased to act, and when it began to do mischief. This observation, therefore, regulated the time of keeping the water on the land; and as this period varied according to the nature of the soil, and the season of the year, it became necessary that he should have such a command of the water at to take if off immediately when he found the state of the land required it.

The effect of these variables appears to make the actions on any pitch entirely dependent on the system immediately upstream. No doubt on a day to day basis it was made to work. Disputes which are now known about because they reached the point of being recorded tend to be about broader issues and in the published literature there appears to be no evidence of mill owners in dispute with those who operated floated meadows. Indeed, apart from the few weeks needed for drowning it was in the farmers' interest to keep the meadows as dry as possible. A floated system sloped imperceptively downhill and in order to drain the water off, either back to the river or directly on to the next system downstream, a 'head of water' had to be created at the top. Where this coincided with a mill two things had to happen.

A mill was wholly designed around the concept that falling water turned the millwheel and drove the machinery; the artificial leat above it left the river and ran straight and level to drop by anything from up to perhaps two metres. At the beginning of the leat the river was held back by a weir, creating the level head of water which would otherwise have simply followed the slope of the river. In practice both the mill apertures and the weir paddles were normally manipulated to provide the miller with an optimum flow of water – neither too much nor too little. However upstream of both these the river might be quite shallow, without the height and power properly to propel the irrigation. To do this both mill and weir had to be at least partly closed. Most material about watermills concentrates on the elevations illustrating the wheel and machinery with the complex systems of gears and hoists. Less common are ground plans showing the passage of water around and through the mill.

Fortunately there is one for Harnham Mill on the Nadder near Salisbury, reproduced as Figure 4.10 (See Chapters 2 and 4). This shows how the three wide elegant arched apertures on the upstream side narrow within the races then widen slightly under the footpath to the outflows downstream. The ground level structure shown (visible in the modern restaurant) confirms that the eastern race housed the wheel, the other two serving as head (controlling) race and eel trap. From downstream the left, western aperture is rectangular rather than arched like the other two, suggesting that it is the third race added only in 1808 (RCHM building 588). Above the mill, from the hotel garden, it is possible, with some care, to see that within the narrowing races there are vertical grooves intended to hold wooden hatch paddles. These paddles are still in position and capable of being operated so that, in theory it should still be possible to reproduce the original practice and reduce or stop the flow so that, in conjunction with closing the nearby weir (and those at Fisherton on the other arm of the river) the river level rises to enable drowning (or irrigating) the intervening meadows.

The apparent good relations between millers and drowners may, of course, simply reflect a lack of known records but drawing up a clear agreement at the outset could no doubt have helped. In 1676 (WSRO 490/894 in Bettey 2005) Lord Coleraine agreed with Elizabeth Clarke of Nunton and Edward Frowde of New Sarum (apparently jointly) to divert water from his paper mill at Nunton on to their meadows subject to strict criteria. It was declared that for an initial consideration of 'Twenty shillings of Current English money' and thereafter of six pounds annually from the latter, both parties were entitled to defined periods of access.

> 'Item, It is Covenanted and Agreed by and between the said parties to these presents that the Water of the said Mill Streame shall be taken and made use of by the said Henry Coleraine and his heires and assignes for ymrpoveing his Meadow Grounds called the Mill Meads, as by the said Elizabeth Clarke and Edward Frowde and their heires and assignes for ymproveing their said Grounds. And the same use or benefit of the Water is to be taken by Turn as followeth, that is to say . . . [Coleraine} . . . to have the turn or stem for first use of the said Water one year, and . . . [Clarke and Frowde] . . . to have the turn or stem the next year, and so from year to year to be continued alterius vicibus [to change alternately]'.

However 'first use' had to be completed by the second of February when the second party could take their turn, although it appears that each could use the other's time if it was not needed. Lord Coleraine also undertook to maintain the 'hatch belonging to the Mill Wheel' and all the other relevant structures and that those diverting the water could 'have liberty to pen and Shutt downe all those hatches belonging to the Mill'. Clearly if this is to be taken literally no paper was going to be produced when the meadows were drowned; it has to be hoped that use during each turn followed the sort of intermittent pattern recorded as good practice by Davis a century or more later. But the reference also tends to confirm that a mill was closed by means of hatches within the races as is still to be seen at Harnham.

Weirs

A modern definition of a weir is simply 'a dam across a stream for raising the level of water above it'. The best a modern dictionary can offer for a hatch is 'a flood-gate or a grated opening is a weir used for a fish trap' and Wiltshire dialect offers only meanings relating to hay making (D & G). In practice both mean the same thing – a dam across a watercourse with, depending on the width, one or more apertures, each with a device that can be raised or lowered to control a flow of water. There are no standard terms. Historically they have varied over time and probably by location. For this work it has been convenient to make the distinction that Weirs control rivers and Hatches control water from the river and on the meadows.

The point is made at Britford, just below Salisbury (see Chapter 2 Figure 2.14) where Sir Thomas Jervois's weir of the 1680s on the Avon is now a modern steel structure, its several plates operated automatically by sensors, responding to river flow. In more traditional fashion the 'Sluice House' contains wooden hatches. Easier to see is the modern steel weir controlling the Nadder above Harnham Mill. In contrast the traditional (but recently restored) two aperture wooden hatch a few metres away in the garden of Rose Cottage controls a main carriage (Figure 4.9). The irrigation systems were totally dependent on weirs, with or without a mill, at least every mile of so to water successive stretches of meadow. Most remain but by no means all are marked on modern maps. All of them will be known to local people but not many are visible from valley crossing points (see Chapter 3). Only a fleeting glimpse while driving past for another purpose led to identifying Haxton Mill (now a brewery) and its associated wooden weir across the Avon, marked as a footbridge on the map (**147491**). This originally created the head of water for meadows down at least to Haxton Bridge and possibly beyond. But, only a few metres from the riverside road through the village, it is practically invisible.

Hatches

Hatches are the main currency of local irrigation. There must have been many thousands operated on the rivers of the chalkland, the majority of which still exist, often in a ruinous state, or have left an archaeological trace. The term 'hatch' was used from the outset in the early seventeenth century, is used by the early twentieth century local writers and is commonplace today. Except to the Ordnance Survey. They adopted the term 'sluice' for their late nineteenth century maps and continue to use the term. The modern definitions generally make the term appropriate but historical researchers are better served by the archaic term. The Old English *haec* must be preferable to the French *escluse* from the Latin *exclusum*, to exclude.

They are all basically much the same but vary widely in size and detail. The overall width of a four aperture hatch on the main carriage at Woodford (Figure 2.6) is 14 feet (measured in 1981). The three intervening stones piers are each some 9 inches wide and thus the four wooden paddles are about 36 inches or, to convert to modern round figure, 90 centimetres. Generally, for obvious reasons, hatches controlling water from the river are of the most robust construction. And, of course, this applies too in the case of what are referred to here as weirs, since a somewhat artificial distinction is being made between similar structures. Those hatches actually on the meadows, usually along the main carriage as at Woodford and under less pressure of water, use smaller timbers and less stone work.

The Avon valley below Salisbury carries the combined flow of the city's five rivers – Ebble, Nadder, Wylye, Avon and Bourne and the weirs and hatches become significantly bigger and more solid. The complex at Standlynch (Figure 2.17) is outstanding both in size and accessibility with a nine aperture weir, sets of hatches at the head of two main carriages, a mill and an eel house. All this heads the three kilometre complex of irrigation downstream, past New Court Farm to Downton. Its seventeenth century creation is well documented, mainly in correspondence between Sir Joseph Ashe, the landowner (in London) and John Snow his local manager. This source was identified in 1982 (Steele 1982) and a wide selection has very recently been transcribed and published by the Wiltshire Record Society (Bettey 2005).

Two documents (WSRO 490/892 and 903) may relate to the Standlynch weir and a relevant contemporary map known to exist but not currently accessible might help to clarify the point. They both however contain interesting details. The first, dated 1691, is

> An account of the Hand [in the sense on 'in hand' or under control] on the River
> Avon at the head of the main Carriage in Charlton grounds of Newcourt farme,
> and several cases [in the sense of enclosing] of Hatches, trunks, burnells [or 'bunnel',
> a conduit], stops and bridges belonging thereunto standing in and upon the main
> carriages in the meadows belonging to the said Newcourt farme for watering the
> said farme meadows.

In this report the most eye catching of 39 observations, mainly about repairs, relates to 'The head case of Hatches of 11 eyes ... thrown down by the flood'. A structure of this size at least suggests the Standlynch site with its modern nine 'eyes'.

The second document, also dated 1691, throws light on dimensions and quantities of materials in 'The Demensions of a Case of Hatches' at a currently unidentifiable point, specifying the amount of good quality ashlar stone (apparently from Fovant) that was needed

> ... to be built ... in the cleare as it appears by the first paper sent to the Quarriars but 20 foot 4 inches, divided into eight eyes of 2 foot 6 inches one half inch in each eye, but since the Quarriars hath been directed, if the stone will hold it, to make them 22 foot in the cleare divided into 8 eyes of 2 foot 9 inches in the clear, with 7 parpin walls [intervening piers, possibly as in the modern 'parpen', a bonding stone], 4 of them to be 14 inches parpin and two of them 15 inches parpin and one of them 18 inches parpin, and in height all of them 8 foot below the rabbit [rebate, or reduction:] and 15 inches above the rabbitt, in all 9 foot 3 inches, and not to hatch backe behind but to hold to be 9 foot 3 inches long each Stop or a little better, all containing of parpin 83 foot in each parpin in the whole'.

It goes on at length in similar vein and one has to trust that the Quarriers knew what was meant. Archaic and confusing it may be but the general thrust is quite clear: this was a major engineering project, and only one of many. In this extract the engineers seem to be revising their calculations to increase the width and strength of probably the three central parpins. The final total length of stone needed in this particular example is shown as 1362 feet, or some 400 metres. Quite how this translates into volume is not apparent.

As an aside from the subject of hatches, linear measurement is also used for land taken for 'Main Channels or Carriages'. For example, in 1666, an 'account of the ground measured . . . in Alderbury Common mead for maine Carrig' includes amongst the 22 items: 'A part of the old Mill Streem the east side next the ham belonging to Withing farme only – 32 [lugs]' and 'John Snow in the east corner of the ham – 4 [lugs]'. The term 'lug' (sometimes 'lugg') is recorded in the late nineteenth century (D & G) as a land measure of 15 feet for mason's work, 18 feet for forestry and 16 feet 6 inches as the, by then, most general use. It appears to be a local variant of the 'rod, pole or perch' familiar from the back covers of school exercise books until the mid twentieth century, meaning 16 feet 6 inches, about five metres. In 1666 the term 'ham' was apparently a variant of 'meadow' (Bettey 2005) but by the late nineteenth century was recorded as a dialect term (D & G) meaning 'a narrow strip of ground by a river, as Mill-Ham' and taking this meaning back to 1842 and 1794. There has been extensive discussion of the derivation and meanings of the word by place-name scholars (summarised in Cole and Gelling 2000, 46-55).

Coming back to hatches there are three useful examples close to the Town Path from Salisbury to Harnham Mill (all illustrated in Figure 4.1 and put in context in Chapter 4). Some 300m from Long Bridge, at the centre point, a small hatch on the right, listed by the managing trust as Sluice 14, controls a spillway (Figure 4.7). The wooden paddle is of standard construction with a solid square section vertical wooden handle attached to several horizontal planks, reinforced with two narrower horizontal struts near the ends. This particular, quite small, paddle is about 2 feet or 0.6 metres wide. The overall width of the structure, including the stone embankments is nearer 1.2 metres. The vertical grooves in the stone embankments holding the paddle in place are reinforced with iron. Timber cross beams contain the simple iron mechanism by which it can be levered up or down. To keep the paddle at a chosen height a retaining claw is secured in one of the circular apertures in the vertical iron plate on the handle. The drowner can operate this from the stone slab footbridge across the narrow channel just behind the hatch. In irrigation terms to use this spillway to return unwanted water to the river is to waste it and, mindful of the previous discussion about drowners and millers, its use by the former to fine tune his efforts might not have pleased the latter.

On the left side of the path is a large irregular hexagonal stone reservoir with Sluice 18 on the far side (Figure 4.8). This is of similar and normal design but significantly bigger than Sluice 14, a paddle width of about one metre, a rather more complex claw securing mechanism and a wider stone footbridge. This hatch has to be bigger and stronger because it controls the flow to the second half of a main carriage and, when shut, has to withstand more water pressure. This is even more apparent with the third example, further along the path, at Rose Cottage. Approaching the cottage a double hatch, Sluice 9, (Figure 5.3) can be seen at the distant end of a section of a main carriage that carries a major water supply. This structure, heavily restored and in good working order, is accessible for close examination when the Trust's Centre in the cottage is open. The two paddles are each of 2.5 metres, with timbers of appropriately sizeable dimensions and a wide wooden footbridge crosses the carriage behind. This gives easy access to the operating mechanism.

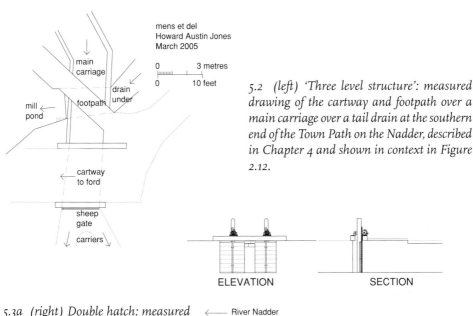

mens et del
Howard Austin Jones
March 2005

0   3 metres

0   10 feet

5.2 (left) 'Three level structure': measured drawing of the cartway and footpath over a main carriage over a tail drain at the southern end of the Town Path on the Nadder, described in Chapter 4 and shown in context in Figure 2.12.

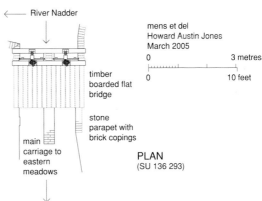

ELEVATION   SECTION

5.3a (right) Double hatch: measured drawing of the double hatch feeding a main carrier through the garden of Rose Cottage at Harnham on the Nadder, described in Chapter 4 and shown in context in Figure 2.12.

← River Nadder

mens et del
Howard Austin Jones
March 2005

0   3 metres

0   10 feet

timber boarded flat bridge

stone parapet with brick copings

main carriage to eastern meadows

PLAN
(SU 136 293)

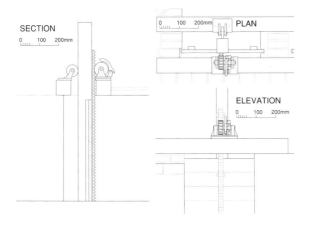

SECTION

0   100   200mm

0   100   200mm   PLAN

ELEVATION

0   100   200mm

5.3b (left) Detail of rack and pinion ironwork at Rose Cottage double hatch.

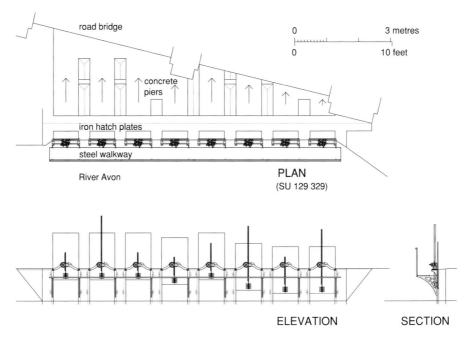

5.4a (above) Iron hatches: measured drawing of the unusual iron structure at Stratford Bridge (129329) illustrated in Figure 3.1d.

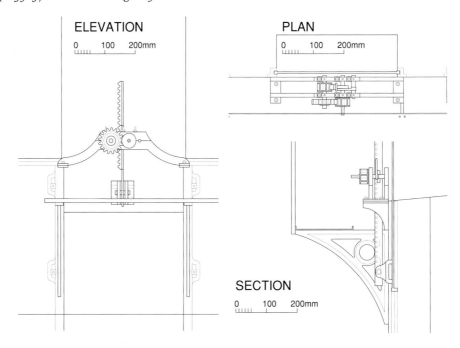

5.4b (above) Iron hatches: detail of rack and pinion ironwork described in the Avon section of Chapter 3; an elegantly cast bracket supports the walkway. Drawings by Howard Jones.

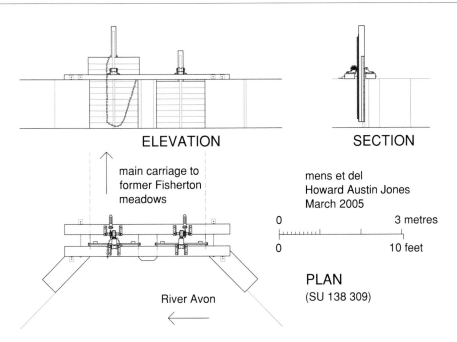

ELEVATION   SECTION

↑
main carriage to
former Fisherton
meadows

mens et del
Howard Austin Jones
March 2005

0   3 metres

0   10 feet

PLAN
(SU 138 309)

River Avon
←

5.5a (above) Double hatch, a wider example than that shown in Figure 5.3: measured drawing of the Blackwell structure (138309) described in Chapter 3; chain shown on the elevation and plan is a modern security device.

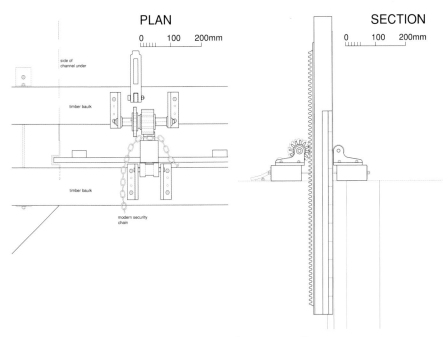

PLAN   SECTION

0   100   200mm   0   100   200mm

side of
channel under

timber baulk

timber baulk

modern security
chain

5.5b (above) Detail of rack and pinion ironwork of the Blackwell structure

In this case the metal work is more complex with a rack and pinion system, the operating and brake pinions held on a square section spindle. The paddle is raised or lowered by applying a giant spanner to the spindle. The claw mechanism on Sluices 14 and 18, and the rack and pinion mechanism on Sluice 9 are the two types illustrated in Figure 5.6 by examples from the main carriage at Woodford (drawn in 1982). Within the characteristics of the two sorts of mechanism the detailed design, manufacturing method and date varies quite widely as the illustration indicates. The metalwork is an interesting aspect of industrial archaeology in its own right and deserves closer study and recording. Wooden hatches perished and were replaced but often the iron work could be re-used. The Warminster iron foundry of B Dutch, in action during the eighteenth and nineteenth centuries produced work that survives on the New Court system above Downton. Their maker's mark no doubt helped create the myth that the irrigated water meadows were created by Dutch engineers, from a country that knew rather a lot about water management. But so did John Snow.

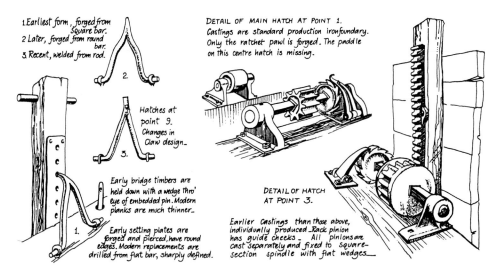

5.6 *Examples of typical iron hatch controls: claw mechanism on left and rack and pinion on right (from Cowan 1982), drawn from hatches on the Woodford system by Althea Dresman.*

Drowning

Once a head of river water had been built up behind a weir, and possibly a mill, it can be used for irrigation by opening the hatches and releasing it on to the meadows. The main hatch lets it into the main carriage from which other hatches feed a series of carriers. The final carriers take it along the top of the ridges that create the corrugated appearance of floated meadows. These carriers diminish in width to vanishing point as the water filling them tips over the edges, down the gently sloping side (or panes) to the intervening drains. The drains between the ridges feed tail drains, more often than not at right angles to the general flow of the meadowland back to the river below the barricade of weir or mill.

From the river the flow of water was driven initially by pressure but increasingly over the length of the pitch by gravity. Thomas Davis knew this and, as quoted above, could say in 1794 that the first concern to deal with the 'flat morass' was to consider how the water was to be carried off and thus to make sure that it was 'thrown up into great ridges'. At Woodford the fall has been calculated as about three feet over the mile or so of the main carriage, which converts rather more easily than is often the case, as about one metre in 1.6 kilometres or a slope of 1/1,600. Davis was writing from the experience of nearly two centuries of practical work that had stood the test of time. But the original learning by experience process was during the seventeenth century as new systems followed each other in quick succession. No doubt mistakes were made and corrected.

Certainly the work between Salisbury and Downton, for which there is now extensive published documentary evidence (some quoted above) suggests this. Towards the end of the century systems were on the whole well established above Salisbury but the next stretch in which landowners were prepared to invest demanded much more massive and expensive engineering than had previously been needed and which did not always work first time. Some of the documents already quoted also refer to replacing work that had been destroyed by floods. More specifically one exchange of letters between Sir Joseph Ashe and John Snow suggests that, in the infancy of instruments, surveying was not always accurate. Indeed, it has to be wondered whether all the construction was done by eye and 'feel'; There do not (yet) appear to be any references to formal surveying.

One document is prefaced by the editor (Bettey 2005)

> John Snow evidently needed to defend himself from the allegations made by his employer, Sir Joseph Ashe. This brief statement illustrates the difficulties he faced with such a large untried project and the problem of accurate surveying to ensure an even flow of water and adequate drainage.

Snow had written (WSRO 490/896) in 1672

> Memorandum: the reasons why the Expence of the before mentioned works came to near duble the expences at first proposed was that when I came on the place

> and found that none of the meads would draw into the river above the fishing
> wyar which caused me to get out the workes otherwise than at first proposed and
> made a drain all up the meads to draw them below the said wyar which made 5 or
> 6 Trunkes more to be made than designed which Trunkes and all the hatches and
> stops proved very chargeable to reason the ground was so boggy where they was
> put in and all the mead so soft that no teems [of horses or oxen] could com near
> the places with anything and the fetching gravill so far and the materials was very
> expensive . . .

and so on. The statement continues and although some of the document is lost,
the message is clear.

Any initial difficulties notwithstanding the work endured. At the end of
the nineteenth century, although the original rationale of the sheep/corn cycle,
the Early Bite and the Golden Hoof may long have gone, hatches and channels
were maintained for hay and cattle. Arthur Street, locally a well known farmer at
Wilton turned writer and journalist in 1931. His lightly disguised fiction about
local farming is a valuable record of the period from the 1870s. Of most value,
however is the straightforward firsthand account in *Round the Year on the Farm*
(Street 1941). This includes a description of the drowner

> cleaning out the drawings, which are the ditches that draw the water from the
> meadows. It is just as important to get the water off as it is to get it on. Stagnant
> water does harm to the grass . . . By now [he] will have cleaned out both carriages
> and drawings, and will be busy placing and stopping. He turns the water into the
> meadows [on perhaps two days a week to accommodate other drowners], and
> then walks along each of the carriages in turn, noticing whether the water flows
> over the sides evenly. To make it do this he places what he calls stops along the
> ditches at intervals, to dam up the water and force it to overflow. He makes these
> 'stops' of the clods that he has cleaned out of the ditches . . . Where he finds the
> water overflowing too fast . . . he picks up some of the loose clods on his **four-
> grained prong** [and builds up the bank].

The highlighted term appears to be the only identified contemporary reference
to any of the specialist implements that a drowner used (see next section).

The drowner was a significant figure on the agricultural scene. There are
references in late nineteenth works that indicate he was employed on a particular
farm as a 'head of department' along with the shepherd, carter, dairyman and so
on. In earlier centuries he seems to have been employed by a co-operative of the
different owners or tenants along a particular stretch of the river. 'An agreement

for a Water Meadow on the River at Burcombe' was presented to the Manorial Court of Burcombe and Ugford on 25 April 1716 (WSRO 2057/M32 in Bettey 2005). It included the provision that

> A workman or head drowner being Chosen betweene the said Mr Pitts and all other the tenants afore to direct and sett out everyone of the said parties their respective stems of drowning as aforesaid.

Presented at the same court on 21 April 1718 was an

> Item, wee doe appoint and order Ambrose Phelpes to be the person or Agent for floating our Meadows with water and drawing it of againe as the said Ambrose Phelpes shall see proper until the next Court to be held for the said Manor in Anno 1719.

The appointment was repeated annually until 1723 when the Court Book ends. Much the same must have happened elsewhere. At Harnham the fragmented occupancy of the water meadows makes it very likely. There is a strong local tradition that Rose Cottage (now used as a Centre by the Harnham Water Meadows Trust) was the 'Drowner's Cottage'. However this description now tends to be avoided as not particularly useful because not understood. 'Waterman's Cottage' makes more practical sense.

Arthur Street also records (Street 1941) a conversation with a Drowner on the meadows in November. After hearing that two meads have been watered and a third was nearly ready he asks if any new hatches are needed, to be told

> Naw. I 'low they'll shammy these round, but thee come wi' across 'ere. Thic bridge awver the main water carriage be tarble [i.e. terribly] feeble. Wants new planks, else we shall have a cow breakin' a leg next spring. I kin put 'em in if you sends some six-inch nails along we' em.

Rather more rigour is nowadays imposed on those engaged on restoration. Where the meadows are restored to working order it is possible to see something that dispels the common assertion that, when drowned, meadows are covered by 'a thin sheet of water'. This conjures up a vision of something like a corrugated ice rink. In fact the water is invisible as it trickles down the side, or pane, of the ridge through grass which by the time it is watered is already quite well grown. In fact a meadow being watered presents a thoroughly untidy appearance.

TOOLS

Although this work is about the floated water meadows of Wiltshire they do not exist in isolation. Nor is the drowning of floated meadows an end in itself. And material so far has dealt successively with a range of individual facets. The intention of this closing section is to pull everthing together in the context of the complete sheep/corn system through its annual cycle, starting in the autumn and using the term 'tools' rather loosely. They are grouped under the headings of drowning, sheep and tools.

Drowning

The cycle starts and finishes with the Drowner. This alarming sounding person has been referred to constantly. Here is a modern assessment published in

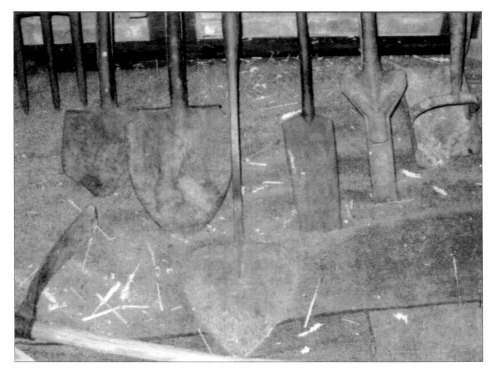

5.7 Drowners' tools: part of the Lackham Museum display, most used for dealing with the irrigation watercourses, some related to cut and covered pipe drains introduced in the nineteenth century. From left to right: clay fork, small then large ditching shovels, turf lifter, two drainage spades, drain ladle; mattock laterally in front (photograph by Tony Pratt).

Wiltshire Archaeological and Natural History Magazine (Atwood 1964).

> . . . no farmer with good shepherd or drowner would dare risk upsetting either of
> them. There is an old Wiltshire saying that 'the shepherd is half the flock'. One
> might say with equal force 'the drowner is half the meadow'. Only the foolish ran
> counter to the wishes of their shepherd or drowner. . . There was generally one
> head drowner in charge of a meadow system in any village or manor. As often as
> not a system was divided in ownership or tenancy between two or three adjacent
> farmer. If so the drowner was employed jointly between them, and when a mill
> intervened, by the Miller as well, for he was also concerned in the use of the river
> water. The drowner, with his highly specialized knowledge and responsibility
> towards these competing interests, thus tended to become even more a law unto
> himself than ... the shepherd. Both men in the old days worked very much together.
> In fact, it was often arranged that when the sheep came down to graze the meadows
> by day, the drowner took charge and handed them back to the shepherd in the
> evening to return to the arable folds.'

Davis, a hundred and fifty years earlier, tells us that

> in the autumn the after grass is eaten off quite bare, when the manager of the
> mead (provincially the drowner) [he is reporting to a government official in London
> who might reasonably not know the local term] begins to clean out the main drain
> . . . make good all the carriages and drains . . . ready for watering . . .

It is interesting that cleaning out the watercourses starts with the drains, in the
same way as they were constructed. In the published literature there is little
about the implements that were to do this. Original documents might do so but
it is fiction (Street 1941, already quoted) that offers a single written reference –
to a 'four-grained prong'. A 1930s dictionary offer a meaning of grain as 'a fork,
a tine, a prong' and also prong as 'a kind of hoe with prongs to break clods'.

Information really only comes from museum collections. Lackham
Museum of Agriculture and Rural Life (at Lacock in Wiltshire) and Breamore
Countryside Museum at Breamore (in Hampshire) both have collections. At
Lackham a display has sixteen implements but includes a number for constructing
nineteenth century field pipe drains. Figure 5.7 shows a number of them.

Routine agricultural practices are not often photographed so it is perhaps
not surprising that the use of these tools appears only to be pictured in one set.
This is held by the Institute of Agricultural History and Museum of English
Rural Life at the University of Reading. Some have been published several times

5.8a   The Drowner: clearing a drain with a ditching shovel and a pronged tool behind, in autumn, the trees still in leaf (© Institute of Agricultural History, Reading).

and have sometimes been captioned as a Drowner working on Britford meadows in the 1930s. One reproduction (Cook and Williamson 1999) has him at Charlton in 1935, the form followed here (Figures 5.8a-b). The first shot shows him clearing an empty channel, probably a drain, using a ditching shovel, with what appears to be a pronged tool in the background. This was probably in the autumn when he had to 'right the works'. In the second he has a coat on, it must be winter, the meadow is being watered and he is using a pronged tool with the shovel standing beside him. The carrier on which he is working illustrates a point made in the previous section that water did not flow as a 'sheet'. It is spilling from the channel because the drains are full; but trickling unobtrusively down the pane just above the roots of the grass.

An oddity is included at this point because it seems to fit nowhere better. A local newspaper article in 1971 (*Western Gazette* in WANHS Cuttings) discusses the craftsmanship of village blacksmiths and refers to the Lackham collection of tools. The piece includes the description of an Archimedes Screw.

> a large wooden tube with an auger or screw inside. This cylinder, when revolved raises water from the river to the irrigation 'carriages' when the level of water in

5.8b The Drowner: attending to a carrier, using the fork with a shovel beside him, the meadow watered in winter (© Institute of Agricultural History, Reading).

> the river is below the meadows . . . in those days this tool was right for its time as it revolved by a horse attached to horse gear.

A device that needed a turning area of this size needed space and it is not easy to visualise how it was laid out. There is no mention of a location but an uncertain and unsourced recollection suggests Britford. The device is held by the museum, and is to be the subject of further research.

Sheep

Several works published in the twentieth century throw light on sheep husbandry well back into the nineteenth (Hudson 1910; Reeves 1978; Smith 1985; Lane-Poole 1976). Much of what is described must have been familiar in earlier centuries but little firsthand anecdotal evidence of this sort comes to light. Amongst the various government sponsored county reports on their agriculture, the one for Wiltshire (Davis 1794 and 1813) has already been quoted extensively in the context of the floated valley meadows, and a part is reproduced. However in his glossary (not reproduced) Davis provides some more details of shepherding and the means that were used.

The Wiltshire Horn breed, almost universally used early into the nineteenth century was hardier that those that followed. This improved stock, bred for a different purpose to the horned type, probably needed more care. For example the late nineteenth century recollections refer to flocks being brought in close to the farmsteads for shelter, particularly during lambing, but there is no indication of this in the 1787 and 1813 reports. The shepherd sometimes needed help, perhaps all the time with very large flocks but his mainstay was his dogs. Tucked away in his Glossary Davis mentions that

> Wiltshire shepherds seldom use crooks, as the sheep are so much easier caught when in fold; but they always use dogs to keep the sheep out of bounds, and by these means are enabled to feed close to an unenclosed piece of standing corn without injuring it.

A later writer describes a scene on Mere Down, 'one of the most extensive and loneliest-looking sheep-walkers in South Wilts ... known as Whitesheet Hill'. He passed three flocks (each with a distinctive bell sound), all without shepherds but with a dog on watch. A shepherd appeared

> and began uttering a curious call . . . instantly the sheep . . . stopped feeding and turned, then all together began running towards him, and when within thirty yards stood still, massed together and all gazing at him, He then uttered a different call, and turning walked away, the dogs keeping with him and the sheep closely following. It was late in the day, and he was going to fold them down at the foot of the slope in some fields half a mile way (Hudson 1910).

Folding involved hurdles, a familiar sight at modern country shows as specialist craftsmen show their skills. Production in earlier centuries was a substantial agricultural industry, large numbers needed to create the temporary moveable enclosures in which sheep were contained. There was a need for this much of the year at night on the arable downlands, and also for a relatively short period on the water meadows when the flock grazed there. This last point is not widely recognised but is stressed by Davis

> The grass [of the water meadows] is daily hurdled out in portions, according to the number of sheep, to prevent their trampling it down; but a few spaces are left in the hurdles, for the lambs to get through, and feed forward in the fresh grass. One acre of good grass will be sufficient for 500 couples for a day . . .

The description in Davis's glossary is still instantly recognisable

Hurdles for sheep-folding – Six feet long, three and a half feet high, made of hazel rods closely wreathed, the upright rods called sails, and the long rods called wreaths (and) Fossels, or Foldshores - The stakes to which the hurdles are fastened with a loose twig-wreath at the top'

The specific figure of 500 ewes and their lambs usefully gives a sense of what shepherding work actually looked like, and in the immediate context here, the quantities of hurdles involved. An acre is 4840 square yards. For those not versed in archaic computation, its square root is 70 yards or some 65 metres. One 70 yard side of a square enclosed needed 35 six foot hurdles, 140 for the whole square. Each adult animal thus had a space of about three metres by three metres for its daily ration of the rich meadow grass. Lambs were being introduced to grass but also still suckling the mothers. It is the watering that presumably makes this density possible and thus the 'added value' that is the economic rationale of the system. The rule of thumb is that each tithing or manor might have between one and two thousand sheep. The higher figure would therefore absorb four acres of meadow grass for each day the flock spent on the meadows, possibly between fifty and sixty days in all.

It also called for probably double the number of hurdles, any exact number depending on a layout to suit different sites and the method and timing of moving them every evening. If at least roughly the same pattern existed at night on the arable, probably some hundreds of hurdles could be in use at any one time. As his 'tools' the shepherd now had his dogs, his own voice and a sufficiency of hurdles. Finally to get his flock from the downland pasture to the arable at night (and back) for most of the year, and to and from the meadows for a shorter period he had droveways or droveroads. There is a description of those at Martin (Lane Poole 1976)

. . . those green ways along which sheep were driven to the downland pastures or the neighbouring markets [Britford, Wilton]. . . they also served as accommodation lanes from which a plough team or waggon could deviate into the open fields on either side; they afforded grazing to horses, cattle and pigs, except for the summer months from May Day to Lammas [1 August] when the corn crops were growing to maturity.

The Manor Court controlled droves. In 1613, at Martin, there was a ruling that tenants had to contribute to the cost of 'a man to catch moles in the droves'. A Court Roll of 1759 confirms that soil could not be removed. Many droves

5.9 The drove road up Harnham Hill (now Old Blandford Road). Both the Nadder and Avon can be seen in the valley with Bishopdown beyond the city of Salisbury. Drawn after 1854 when All Saints' Church, Harnham was built, and published in 1872 (The original is creased).

remain as wide green lanes and some have become roads, still often identifiable by the very wide verges and, in places, steep winding passage. A lane now leading to a disused chalkpit at West Harnham formerly wound up the slope of the downs. It's eponymous pond has gone but it is still memorably called Carrion Pond Drove. On the West Harnham Inclosure map of 1787 this drove is very clear. It is the widest way marked, a mile and a quarter (say two kilometres) south from the meadows past the chalk pit and (nowadays a footpath across a golf course) joining the Shaftesbury Drove to the west.

Hay

Once the shepherd's charges had chewed off the early grass the meadows could be left for hay. The water channels, after having been dug out, would by now have begun to silt up and provide, in themselves, rich soil for the grass. This can be seen today on the Harnham meadows at Salisbury, The main carriages tend to have water in them most of the time but the carriers and drains are only watered intermittently, recreating historical accuracy if only by default. As restoration has continued the channels have been dug by JCB, a tracked vehicle operating a hydraulically controlled bucket. The vehicle can move along the side of each ridge with minimal damage operating the bucket to each side. Thus the old drowner's tools are replaced. But the system does not remain clean and tidy for long. The grass regenerates very quickly so that when it came to haymaking a complete meadow had to be cut, channels and all.

Making hay by hand in an uncertain climate was a chancy business. Cut grass had to be evenly and sufficiently dried to safely stand being built up into a rick. Doing this too soon risked souring the hay or heating and maybe catching fire. Delaying too long meant nutrients lost or hard work destroyed by rain. And this was a labour intensive business with scythes and rakes. The 1893 dictionary of Wiltshire words (D and G) contains a very full entry

> Hay-making. Grass as it is mown lies in SWATHES; then it is TURNED, preparatory to being TEDDED, or SPREAD; then raked up into lines called HATCHES, which may be either SINGLE HATCH or DOUBLE HATCH, and are known in some parts as WALLOES; next SPREAD and HATCHED UP again, and put up in small FOOT-COCKS, COCKS or POOLS; after being thrown about again it is WAKED UP into long WAKES, or ROLLERS, and if not made temporarily into SUMMER-RICKS, is then carried.

The entry goes to quote an apparently ironic comment that the hay is 'nearly worn out with handling before they get it to the rick' and to record some other local terms.

The description above is of a general nature and does not deal with what must have been special difficulties on the irrigated land, making it even more labour intensive. However having coped with scything and raking either across or along the ridges and furrows the next task was to make temporary ricks or carry the hay off. Described in the twentieth century (Street 1941)

> The old fashioned method was to rake the swathes by hand into rows wide enough apart to permit the horse and wagon to pass along between them. Then a man could pitch up the hay on a hayfork from either side of the wagon. There would be two men pitching the hay from the ground, two men on the wagon building the load, and a lad driving the horses between the rows.

This system survived into the twentieth century on smallholdings, one such described at Breamore (in Hampshire on the lower Avon) about 1950 (G Ponting 2004). In the same work is a first hand record of the Allen Scythe, a petrol-driven two wheeled hand-operated grass cutter. The cutter bar, similar to a modern hedge trimmer, could be set to left or right so that the machine would run along the meadow panes without its wheels damaging the channels. It is often observed that the meadows system fell into disuse because it was too labour intensive and machinery could not do the jobs needed. The machine apparently could and was used elsewhere, at least around Breamore.

The load was then driven to the rick, either on the meadows or near the farm. No description has been found of how a cart or wagon actually negotiated the dry watercourses; a deep main carriage for example could resemble a tank trap. Maybe, of course, they didn't, and the hay had to be taken by hand to some convenient point. Sometimes, too, the hay crop was lost. Written from lightly disguised personal experience *The Gentleman of the Party* (Street 1936) records a fictional rainy summer when

> harassed employees turned his seeds hay sixteen times between the storms . . . The water meadow hay was an even worse job. It was laid badly by the rain before cutting . . . the operation more costly than usual. Again the useless turning and tedding was done, until the river Bindon flooded the meadows and carried the bulk of the hay downstream where it blocked the hatches of Mr Martin's neighbours and caused further trouble.

Mr Martin wished good riddance to bad rubbish and relished that it was now 'old Jack Warner's blasted worry, thank God'

If there were cows to be grazed this could be done on the water meadows after the hay was gathered. But the real end of the cycle, before the Drowner could start again, was carrying the hay from the meadows, using the most distinctive tools of all, a cart or a Wiltshire wagon. Most countries or areas had their own pattern of wagon but any wagon was a complex structure, particularly regarding the stability of the wheels and the way in which the body was supported on the forecarriage. This had to turn in a horizontal plane, the smaller front wheels able to turn below the bed of the wagon. A Wiltshire wagon was possibly more distinctive than most with it high wide 'raves' over the rear wheels. These increased the loading capacity, as did the hay ladders that could be fitted front and back.

Figure 5.10 shows an empty Wiltshire wagon in 1959 (by then probably very old) and then the same one loaded with an impossible looking amount of hay to a height of perhaps five metres, the wagon has strayed into Hampshire because the scene, again, is at Breamore on the Avon below Downton, photographed in his school days by an author who in 2004 published a work on

5.10 A Wiltshire wagon at Breamore in 1959 and the same wagon loaded with hay (from Ponting 2004, p.90).

'growing up in the Hampshire countryside in the 1940s and 1950s' (G Ponting). His photographs show the wagon pulled by a single horse between the shafts, said to be normal practice. However more than a century earlier Constable's version in the foreground to Salisbury Cathedral had three horses in line. In a similarly fictitious setting (but no less useful a source, Street 1936) George Simmons, a farm worker all his life, is the 'gentleman' of the title. In 1872 he was twelve years old and had

> learnt to drive three horses at length when the dung was hauled out from the yards, . . . walked endless miles up and down leading a horse which was pulling a horse-hoe through . . . turnips. In June he drove enormous loads of hay from the water meadows to the stack yard. This was a most enjoyable job, because loads had to be driven through the river, which meant that Georgie rode the trace horse proudly into the ford.

The waggon he was drawing was elegantly designed and superbly functional, here playing its part in a system that had the same characteristics. A fitting note on which to end this section and this work.

Annex 1
Rose Cottage

Rose Cottage is at the Harnham end of the Town Path at Salisbury, described in Chapter 4. Miss Jane Foster lived in the cottage from 1951 until her death in 2004. She wrote this account for the Friends of the Harnham Water Meadows Trust Newsletter (number 23, spring 2003). The cottage was bought by the Trust in 2005 to house a warden on the meadows and to provide a base for information and education.

Rose Cottage was condemned in 1938 – the reasons – no damp proof course, two feet below the level of the river, no water or sanitation laid on. Apparently this had not bothered the generations of previous inhabitants, the last of which was a family called Evans - the father being in charge of the hatches and meadows irrigation.

We knew none of this, when, also in 1938 we moved to Salisbury from Harrogate. My father, who had worked for the West Riding County Council at the County hall in Wakefield as an architect and land surveyor, took a job with the Southern Command at Radnor House, opposite St. Paul's church - designing army huts rather than farm cottages! From 1938 to the end of the war we rented a roomy three storey semi-detached house at the bottom of Devizes Road. After the war the landlord had plans to turn it and its neighbour into flats. So my parents started to look for 'a small house with a large garden' as a retirement home. Rose Cottage was on the market, owned by Mrs Fox Pitt who was living there, before and during the war she owned The Old Mill Hotel and restaurant, the Old Mill Flats and the adjoining cottage, but had already sold those properties. She had acquired the Water Meadows on the far side of the storm channel [main carriage] to turn into a garden. She may have intended to make it a permanent home but was unable to obtain planning permission for alterations.

At that time the cottage consisted of two small downstairs rooms. A staircase with steps of uneven height went up to a wide landing with a door leading into a bedroom. (The Evans were said to have had eight children!) There was also a small lean-to kitchen, a 'recent' addition about fifty years old.

I was teaching away from Salisbury throughout the war and for several years after but did go once when on holiday while the cottage was in that original state. Mrs Fox Pitt,

Rose Cottage from the opposite side of the river, with footpath and weir in the foreground.

a somewhat eccentric lady, was mainly concerned on that occasion with a bantam which had fallen in the water (the channel normally had a regular if low flow through it). The bird was reposing, warmly wrapped, in front of the little kitchen boiler. (I believe it died - one can only speculate on its ultimate fate!)

Mrs Fox Pitt had been perfectly frank about the condemned status of the cottage, and had a robust view of the facilities - plenty of firewood could be dredged from the river, a standpipe and tap at the end of Island Cottage garden for drinking water and a galvanised iron hut outside for other essential needs. My mother thought the prospect hopeless, my father could see possibilities so the purchase went ahead. Sure enough, along came an official notice saying the building had to be demolished in such & such a time - giving the reasons (as mentioned earlier). My father's response was to put the town council in the county court. He spoke from 11 o'clock until 20 to 1.0 using his, by then, quite extensive experience (he was 66) to take each reason for demolition to cite precedents against them. He had the knowledge and memory to refer to 'sub-section so and so of the eighteenth hundred and something housing act etc.'

For example he took the 'two feet below river level' saying there were houses sixteen feet below the river Ouse. He said he could see the 'Old judge' smiling (his phrase, he was a much younger man) and at the end, the judge, after commenting that he had been brought up in a cottage without a damp proof course and it hadn't done him any harm, quashed the demolition order and said we could spend £100 (worth considerably more in 1946 than it is now). This was only the beginning, we had to keep on applying for licences, builders would come for three weeks and stay away three months through shortage of suppliers or trying to cope with many other customers.

There were also post-war restrictions. We could have the living room floor repaired but not renewed, so the carpenter put new boards everywhere, except for a patch by the fireplace. When a few weeks after we moved the backlegs of a chair went through the rotten wood that was replaced also!

We were able to have an extension to the living room, because it was replacement of an 'existing building' - which was an old wooden shed at the side of the house. After about four years we moved in, in January 1951. All the family (parents, two sisters and I) contributed to the cost. I started teaching at the old St Paul's school that autumn so remember what life was like during our early years at the cottage.

At night think 'dark', the circle of the horizon broken only by two patches of light, the station and the old Infirmary. Coming from the town it was like a country lane. No cathedral illumination, buildings in the close not so near the river and masked by trees, no obvious street lights along Harnham Road, Old Blandford Road, Middle Street (housing development at Harnham had only just started after the war) where the 'Old Mill Gardens' houses now face us across the river was the Old Mill garden. No Churchfields. In the daytime we could look along the river and see Bemerton Church. Town Path was narrower and rougher really only the edge of the fields fenced off. Long Bridge was a flat plank structure, on the same level as the path. It did have rails both sides but was barely wide enough for two to walk abreast.

The darkness was no problem to us, we had been coping quite cheerfully in the blackout a few years before. There was the bonus of seeing the stars clearly, Orion and Sirius sparkling on winter nights, or the full moon shining on the pool outside. They are still there, but the effect is much diminished.

There were many fewer people in Harnham, but the path was well used, even at night, by railway and P.O. sorting office staff, people walking dogs or going to and from the town. It was useful to have a torch to switch on to alert approaching cyclists or pedestrians of one's presence. Some carried lighted cigarettes, giving a little red glow in the darkness.

Changes have happened gradually over the years, a good one being greater appreciation of the achievements of the past. In the case of Rose Cottage its rise from condemnation to Grade II listed status!

Annex 2
Extracts from Thomas Davis's work of 1813

Annotations apart, the whole of this section is reproduced from the publication General View *of the Agriculture of Wiltshire drawn up for the consideration the Board of Agriculture and Internal Improvement by Thomas Davis, 1813 edition. There are three long extracts relating to the south of Wiltshire, as chalk country dealing with feeding on common land, irrigation, and sheep. Each is preceeded by the page numbers from which it has been taken, in square brackets as are the annotations.*

[pages 18-21]

SECT. III – GENERAL CUSTOM OF FEEDING COMMONABLE LANDS.

The custom of feeding the commonable lands, and the number of stock each commoner (or occupier of a yard land) has a right to put on them, varies in the district, but in general it is as follows:

Sheep Commons – The common sheep-down is open for the common flocks during the summer and autumn.

The unsown or summer-field is also open till it is ploughed for wheat: after that the sheep have only the down till the harvest is over. When the corn fields are clear, the flock has those fields and the down till the winter obliges the owners to give them hay.

Thomas Davis of Longleat, a portrait from his own 1813 work.

Until this period, they are folded on the arable fields in a common fold; but when they begin to eat hay, every commoner finds his own fold and his own hay, the common shepherd feeding and folding the whole. This is the ancient custom of managing the sheep stock in the district; but latterly, as the value of stock has become more known to a South Wiltshire farm, the tenants of common fields have introduced the practice of folding their separate flocks on their own lands, thereby placing their sheep under the immediate care of their own servants, rather than entrusting them to a common shepherd, whose neglect or partiality made his attentions inadequate to the care of the whole. When the ewes are near yeaning, the owners take them home to their enclosed meadows, and by the time all the lambs have dropped, the water-meadows are ready to take them to grass.

In some instances the water-meadows are common for sheep stock in the spring, are mown in small known lots in the summer, and are fed by the common herd of cows in the autumn: in others, these meadows are wholly private property. Whilst the water-meadows are open, the sheep are folded on the barley land, and by the time the water-mead grass is eaten, and the barley sown, the summer field (especially if it be sown with ray-grass) is ready to receive the sheep, where they generally remain till near shearing time, when they go to the down until the stubble-fields are broken, at which time (perhaps about the middle of September) the rams are usually put to the ewes. The rams are provided, and the common shepherd is paid, at the joint expense of the commoners.

As this state of commonage, where there must necessarily be a great scarcity of winter food, requires a reduction of the sheep stock before winter, it is customary to sell off the old ewes and the wether [castrated ram] lambs about Michaelmas, and to put out the ewe lambs to be wintered either on pasture land or turnips, in other parts of the same, or in an adjacent county [part of the local area]. These lambs are usually put out from the 10th October till the 5th of April, and the price is seldom lower than 7s., in some instances as high as 10s. per head; and yet after this diminution of the flock, the common-field farmers are not unfrequently obliged to buy hay for the remainder, and to fetch it from a distance of ten or fifteen miles.

Cow Commons – Cow commons (called cow-downs) are frequent in the undivided parts of the district, but not general. They were more numerous formerly, many of them having been converted at different times into sheep downs by consent of the commoners. These cow downs are usually the best and most level parts of the down lands, and are worth from 6s. to 12s. per acre.

The common herd of cows begin to feed the cow downs early in May, usually Holyrood-day, and finish when the fields are clear of corn.

At the beginning and end of the season, they are driven to the down in the morning and brought back in the evening; but in the heat of summer they are only kept on the down during the night, and in the morning they are brought back into the villages, where they feed on the lanes and small marshes by the river side, if such there be, till after the evening milking. When the stubble-fields are open, the cows have a right to feed them jointly with the sheep, and if there are common meadows, whether watered meadows or not, they have an exclusive right to feed them till the end of the commoning season, usually St. Martin's-day, 11th November, O.S. [old style: pre-1752] when the owners take them home to the straw-yards. The cow-down, when the cows leave it to go to the stubble-fields, becomes common for the sheep flock during all, or a certain part of the winter, when it is again laid up for the cows.

[pages 116-132]

SECT. IV. – IRRIGATION

IRRIGATION, which is justly called by Mr. Kent, 'the greatest and most valuable of all improvements,' was generally introduced into this district at the latter end of the seventeenth, or at the beginning of the eighteenth century. Many of the most valuable and best formed meadows, particularly those in Wyley Bourne, were made under the directions of one farmer Baverstock, of Stockton, between the years 1700 and 1705.

An imperfect scheme of watering had undoubtedly been practiced before that period. Its introduction indeed into this district may perhaps be almost coeval with the practice of sheep-folding, with which it is intimately connected; but the regular mode in which those systems are now conducted is certainly not very ancient. Many old farmers, who have died within the memory of man, remembered when neither the water-meadow nor the sheep-fold was managed on any regular plan.

[Modern study of 17th-century documentary evidence allows us to correct this analysis. In the 'district', that is the south of the county floated meadows were extensively established by 1700. He may be right about the sheep folding.]

Theory of Water-Meadows.
The idea of watering meadows, as far as it relates to the bringing of water upon the land, was taken from nature. It must have been always observed, that winter floods produced fertility, provided the water did not remain long.

The idea of taking the water off the land, and bringing it on again at will, is the suggestion of art; and the knowledge of the proper time of doing this, is the result of observation.

A water-meadow is a hot-bed for grass. In what manner water acts upon land, so as to accelerate vegetation, is a philosophical problem, which it is not the farmer's province to solve: – it was sufficient for him to know that the fact was so. Observation on the effects of water so brought on, soon showed him at what period its food properties ceased to act, and when it began to do mischief. This observation, therefore, regulated the time of keeping the water on the land; and as this period varied according to the nature of the soil, and the season of the year, it became necessary that he should have such a command of the water as to take it off immediately when he found the state of the land required it. This produced by degrees that regular disposition of water-carriages and water-drains which, in a well laid out meadow, bring on and carry off the water as systematically as the arteries and veins do the blood in the human body.

As water-meadows are totally unknown in some parts of the kingdom, and but very partially known in others, and as there is perhaps no county in which the system of watering meadows is so well understood and practiced in South Wiltshire, we shall here speak a little more fully of their nature and properties.

Nature and Properties of Water- Meadows. -It has been already premised, that the grand principle of a water-meadow is the power of bringing on and carrying off the water at pleasure; and if this object can be accomplished, it is not material what the shape of the meadow is, nor that the disposition of the trenches, (provincially called 'the works of the meadow') should be uniform; but as very little land can be entirely commanded by water, unless its inequalities are reduced by manual labour, it has been found convenient to adopt two kinds of water-meadows, one for land lying on declivities, which must in general be watered from springs or small brooks, and the other for low land near rivers, which is watered from those rivers.

The first kind is called in Wiltshire, *a catch-work meadow*; and the latter, *a flowing meadow*: the latter is the most general kind in this district.

It is impossible to give any intelligible written description of the mode of making these meadows: this operation must be seen, to be properly understood.

[To the best of this author's knowledge no example of a catch-work system has reliably been shown to exist in modern times. This description may prompt an identification. There is a suggestion that it was in use at the Jones's Mill site: see the discussion in Chapter 2.]

Catch-work Meadows described. – But to elucidate the distinction between two kinds of meadow, and to give some idea of what are the situations in which they may be introduced, it may be necessary to remark, that the 'catch-work meadow' is made by turning a spring, or small stream, along the side of a hill, and thereby watering the land between the new cut (or, as it is provincially called, the 'main carriage') and the original water-course, which now becomes the 'main drain.' this is sometimes done, in particular instances, merely by making the new cut level, and stopping it at the end, so that when it is full, the water may run out at the side, and flood the land below it. But as the water would soon cease to run equally for any great length, and would wash the land out in gutters, it has been found necessary to cut small parallel trenches, or carriages, at distances of 20 to 30 feet, to catch the water again; and each of these being likewise stopt at its end, lets the water over its side, and distributes it until it is caught by the next, and so on, over all the intermediate beds, to the main drain at the bottom of the meadow, which receives the water, and carries it on to water another meadow below, or, if it can be so contrived, another part of the same meadow on a lower level.

To draw the water out of these parallel trenches or carriages, and lay the intermediate beds dry, a narrow deep drain crosses them at right angles, at about every nine or ten poles length [some fifty yards], and leads from the main carriage at top of the main drain at the bottom of the meadow.

When this meadow is to be watered, the ends of the carriages adjoining the cross-drains are stopt with turf dug on the spot, and the water is thrown over as much of the meadows as it will cover well at a time, which the watermen call a *pitch of work*; and when it is necessary to lay this pitch dry, they take out the turfs, and let the water into the drains, and proceed to water another pitch.

This kind of water-meadow is seldom expensive; the stream of water being usually small and manageable, few hatches are necessary; and the land lying on a declivity, much less manual labour is required to throw the water over it regularly, and particularly to get it off again, than in the flowing meadows. The expense of making such a meadow is usually from £3 to £5 per acre: the improvement frequently from 15s. an acre to at least 40s.; the annual expense of keeping up the works and watering the meadow, which is usually done by the acre, seldom so high as 10s. 6d. per acre.

Flowing Meadows described. – In the formation of the 'flowing meadows,' much more labour and system are required. The land applied to this purpose being frequently a flat morass, the first object to be considered is, how the water is to be *carried off* when once brought on; and in such situations, this can seldom be done without throwing the land up in high ridges, with deep drains between them.

A main carriage is taken out of the river, at a level high enough to command the tops of the ridges, and the water is brought by small trenches, or carriages, along the top of each ridge, and, by means of moveable stops of turf or earth, is thrown over or on each side, and received by the drains below, whence it is collected into a main drain, and carried on to water other meadows, or lower parts of the same meadow. A tier of these ridges, watered at on time, is called *a pitch of work.* The size of the ridges varies according to the supply of water, but in general they are about 30 or 40 feet wide, and 9 or 10 poles long [some 150 ft].

It is obvious from this description, that as the water is here used only once in *one pitch*, this method is only applicable to large streams, or to vallies subject to floods; and that as the ridges must be formed by manual labour, and the hatches requisite to command the water on rivers, must be much more expensive than those on small brooks. The first cost of the following meadow is considerably greater than that of the more simple method first described.

The expense of making a *flowing* meadow will vary from 12l. to 20l. per acre, according to the difficulty of the ground, and the quantity of hatch-work required; but the increase in the value of the land by this operation, is astonishing. The abstract value of a good water-meadow may fairly be stated at 5l. per acre; but its value when taken as part of a farm, and particularly of a sheep-breeding farm, is almost beyond computation; and when such a meadow is once made, it may be said to be made for ever; the whole expense of keeping up the works and watering it, not exceeding 7s. per acre yearly, and the expense of the hatches, if they are well made at first, being a mere trifle for many years.

Supposed Quantity of Water-Meadows in this District. – The number of acres of land in this district under this kind of management, has been computed, and with a tolerable degree of accuracy, to be between 15 and 20,000 acres.

Indeed it has been found so very beneficial, that very few spots of land capable of being watered, remain other wise, unless where some water-mill stands in the way, or where some person, who has the command of the water above, refuses to let it be taken out of its natural course to water the lands below.

Some new meadows might be made, and very great and beneficial alterations in the old ones, if a plan could be adopted to get the command of water where necessary for this purpose, and particularly in the case of water-mills: a remedy for this will be afterwards proposed.

'Water-Meadows do not make a Country Un-healthy.' – It has been alleged, by those who know very little of water-meadows, that they render the country unhealthy, by making the water stagnant. Daily observation shows that this opinion is erroneous, and the reason is obvious. We have already observed, that a water-meadow is 'a hot-bed for grass;' the action of the water on the land excites a fermentation; that fermentation would no doubt finally terminate in putrefaction; but the moment putrefaction takes place, vegetation ceases. Every farmer knows the commencement of this putrefaction, by the scum the water leaves on the land; and if the water be not immediately taken off, the grass will rot, and this meadow will be supplied for the season. The very principle of water-meadows will not allow water to be stagnant; it must be always kept in action, to be of any service. But besides this, many of the best meadows were, in their original state, a stagnant unwholesome morass: the draining such land, and making it so firm that the water may be taken off at will, must surely, instead of injuring a country, essentially contribute to the salubrity of the air.

'Great Advantages arising from Water-Meadows.' – It is frequently asked, how it comes to pass that, although water-meadows are so useful as to be almost an indispensable appendage to a South Wiltshire farm, yet, in other counties where they are not known, the want of them is not felt? nay, that there are even in this district many parishes which have none, and which breed lambs without them. To this I answer, that the fair question is not, 'how do other countries manage without them; ' but, 'how could the farmers of this district, who are so fortunate as to have water-meadows, pursue their present system of sheep-breeding, if those meadows were taken away?' – a system, which I do not hesitate to say, is more profitable to themselves, their landlords, and the community at large, than any other that could be substituted in its room. This question cannot perhaps be answered better, than by exhibiting the contrast between those who have water-meadows, and those who have none, in the same district.

Every farmer who keeps a flock of sheep, and particularly a breeding flock, in so cold and late springing a district as South Wilts, knows and feels the consequences of the month of April - that month between hay and grass - in which he who has not water-meadows for his ewes and lambs, frequently has nothing. The ewes will bring a very good lamb with hay only: perhaps a few turnips are preserved for the lambs, which, is a very favourable season, may last them through March; but they are then obliged to go to hay again; the ewes shrink their milk, the lambs 'pitch and get stunted,' and the best summer food will not recover them. To prevent this, recourse is had to feeding the grass of those dry meadows that are intended for hay, the young clovers, and frequently the your wheat; in fact, every thing that is green. And who will pretend to estimate what is the loss that a farmer suffers by this expedient?

The ray-grass on the exposed parts of this district, is seldom 'a bite' for the sheep till May-day. If the season should permit any turnips to be kept till that time, which can seldom be depended upon . . . They are not only of little nourishment to the stock, but they exhaust the land, so as to prejudice the succeeding crop; and it ought to be remarked, by the way, that in many parts of this district, the soil is not at all favourable to the production of turnips. It therefore necessarily follows, that a farmer under these circumstances has no certain resource to support his stock during this month, but hay; and even in that he is sometimes disappointed, by having been obliged in the preceding spring to feed all the land which he has laid up for a hay crop. He is then under the necessity of buying hay, and that frequently at the distance of many miles; and to add to this distress at this critical time, his young ewes are brought home from wintering, to be kept nearly a month on hay alone.

In this month, which so often ruins the crops and exhausts the pockets of those sheep-breeding farmers who have no water-meadows, the water-mead farmers may be truly said to be 'in clover.' They train up their dry meadows early, so as almost to ensure a crop of hay; they get their turnip land fed off in time to prepare it for barley, and they have the great advantage of a rich fold to manure it; they save a month's hay, and have no occasion to touch their field grass till there is a good bite for their sheep; and their lambs are as forward at May-day, as those of their less lucky neighbours are at Midsummer; and after all, they are nearly certain of a crop of hay on their water-meadows, be the season what it may.

Management of Water-Meadows. – The management of water-meadows, as well as it can be described in an account necessarily concise, is as follows:- in the autumn the after-grass is eaten off quite bare, when the manager of the mead (provincially the *drowner*) begins to clean out the main drain, and the main carriage, and to 'right up the works,' that is, to make good all the carriages and drains which the cattle have trodden in, so as to have one tier or pitch of work ready for drowning. This is immediately put under water (if water be plenty enough), whilst the drowner is preparing the next pitch.

In the following meadows, this work ought to be done, if possible, earl enough in the autumn to have the whole meadow ready to catch the first floods after Michaelmas: the water being the first washing of the arable lands on the sides of the chalk-hills, as well as of the dirt from the roads, is then thick and good.

The length of this autumnal watering cannot be precisely stated, as much depends upon situations and circumstances; but if water can be commanded in abundance, the custom is, to give the meadows a 'through good soaking at first,' perhaps for a fortnight or three weeks, with an intermission of two or three days during that period; and sometimes for the space of two fortnights, allowing an interval of a week between them. The works are then made as dry as possible, to encourage the growth of the grass. The first soaking is to make the land sink and pitch close together; a circumstance of great consequence, not only to the quantity, but to the quality of the grass, and particularly to encourage the shooting of the new roots, which the grass is continually forming, to support the forced growth above.

While the grass grows freely, a fresh watering is not wanted; but as soon as it flags, the water must be repeated for a few days at a time; always keeping this fundamental rule in view, 'to make the meadows as dry as possible after every watering; and to take off the water the moment any scum appears upon the land, which shews that it has already had water enough.'

Some meadows that will require the water for three weeks in October, and the two following months, will not perhaps bear it a week in February or March, and sometimes scarcely two days in April and May.

In the catch-meadows, which are watered by springs, the great object is, to keep the works of them very dry between the intervals of watering; and as such situations are seldom affected by floods; and generally have too little water, it is necessary to make the most of the water, by catching and rousing it as often as possible; and as the upper works of every pitch will be liable to get more water than those lower down, a longer time should be given to the latter, so as to make them as equal as possible.

Custom of Feeding Water-Meadows with Sheep. – We have already remarked, that the great object of an early crop of water-meadow grass, in this district, is to enable the farmer to breed early lambs.

As soon as the lambs are able to travel with the ewes (perhaps about the middle of March), the flock is put into the water-meadows. Care is, or ought to be taken, to make them as dry as possible for some days before the sheep begin to feed them; and on account of the quickness of the grass, it is not usual to allow the ewes and lambs to go into them with empty bellies, nor before the morning dew is gone. The general hours of feeding are from ten or eleven in the morning, till four or five in the evening, when the sheep are driven to the fold, which at that time of the year is generally on the barley-fallow.

The grass is daily hurdled out in portions, according to the number of sheep, to prevent their trampling it down; but a few spaces are left in the hurdles, for the lambs to get through, and feed forward in the fresh grass. One acre of good grass will be sufficient for 500 couples for a day: the great object is, to make the water-meadow grass last till the barley sowing is finished.

Meadow laid up for Hay. – As soon as this first crop of grass is eaten off by the ewes and lambs, the water is immediately thrown over the meadows, and they are then made perfectly dry, and laid up for hay. Six weeks are generally sufficient for this crop: it seldom requires eight, and there have been instances of great crops being produced in five weeks.

Nature of Water-Meadows Hay. – The grass of water-meadows being frequently large and coarse in its nature, it is necessary to cut it young; and if it be well made, the hay is of a peculiarly nourishing milky quality, either for ewes or dairy cows.

In some instances the water-meadows are laid up for a second crop; but this is only done when hay is scarce: not that the practice is supposed to be injurious to the land; but the grass being of that herbaceous soft nature, takes so much time to dry, that the hay is seldom at that season well saved. The grass is of much greater value to be fed with dairy cows. A flush of after-grass so early and so rank, will be precisely of the same comparative service to the dairy, as the spring feed has been described to be to the ewes and lambs. The cows remain in the meadows till the drowner begins to prepare for the winter watering.

Water-Meadows safe for Sheep in the Spring, but will rot them in the Autumn. – Water-meadows are considered to be perfectly safe for sheep in the spring, even the land that would rot them if it were not watered; but in the autumn, the best water-meadows are supposed to be dangerous. This, at present, is a mystery in the operations of Nature; and a discovery of the reason might perhaps tend, in some measure, to a discovery of the causes of the rot in sheep. But he circumstances itself is rather an advantage than otherwise to this district, as it obliges the farmers to keep a few dairy cows to feed the water-meadows in the autumn, and to provide artificial grasses, or other green crops, for their sheep during that period.

Proper Soils for Water-Meadows.
From what we have so repeatedly urged on the necessity of making water-meadows, dry as well as wet, every reader must have inferred the advantage of having them, if possible, on a warm absorbent bottom.

The bottom or subsoil of the water-meadow, is of much more consequence than the quality or depth of the top-soil. But it must not be inferred, that land whose substratum is peat or clay, cannot be considerably improved by watering, for there are many good meadows on such soils; yet it is proper to remark, that they are not so desirable, on account of the difficulty of drawing the water from them, and making them firm enough to bear treading.

A loose gravel, or what is perhaps still better, a bed of broken flint, with little or no intermixture of earth, wherever it can be obtained, is the most desirable bottom.

In many of the best meadows in this district, where the substratum is a warm absorbent gravel, or a bed of broken flint, the soil is not six inches in depth, and yet is quite sufficient, in seasons when water is plenty; as the grass will root in the warm gravel in preference to the best top-soil whatever, and such meadows always produce the earliest grass. Nor is it very material of what kind of grasses the herbage is composed, when the meadow is made: if there be always a sufficient quantity of water at command, that kind of grass will predominate which best aggress with the soil and the water; but if the supply of water be irregular, those grasses will prevail which can bear wet and dry; and it is a circumstance worthy of our notice, that some of the worst grasses in their native state, will become the best when made succulent by plenty of water.

SECT. V. – LONG GRASS MEADOWS.

NATURE has given us a striking lesson on this subject in this district, viz. in the two small meadows at Orcheston (a village lying about six miles to the N. W. of Amesbury), usually called the 'Long Grass Meads.'

These meadows adjoin each other, and contain together only two acres and an half; and yet crop they produce, in some seasons, is so immense, and of so good a quality, that the tithe hay of them was once sold (according to the information of the tenant) for the sum of five guineas.

Much has been said and little understood about these meadows, and the grass they produce. Many proposals and attempts have been made to propagate the grass, and many skilful botanists have returned from the spot, without discovering which was the long grass, so different is its appearance at different seasons.

It has been, however, lately discovered by Mr. Sole, of Bath, and communicated to the Bath Society, that the greatest part of the herbage of these meadows is nothing more than the 'black couch,' or 'couchy bent,' the *agrostis stolonifera*, one of the worst grasses, in its native state, which the kingdom produces, and the peculiar of the farmers of this district. It usually abounds in such arable land as is too poor to bear the white couch (*triticum repens*), and is the general and almost only herbage of the old, burn-beaked, worn-out downs, and in that situation is so coarse and wiry, that no cattle will eat it: it forms a thick tough covering over the lands, which preserves itself, and destroys every thing else. But in these meadows, when fed abundantly with water, it is of a juicy nourishing quality, and makes the most desirable hay in the district, particularly for sheep. These meadows lie in the upper part of the bourne that runs from Tilshead to Stapleford, and, in some winters, the rivulet that passes through them is very inconsiderable. They are not laid out in any regular form for watering, the supply of water being too partial; but they depend entirely upon the floods; and being situated at a sharp turn of a narrow part of the valley, the water makes an eddy, and deposits its sediment upon them. The substratum of these meadows is an almost entire bed of loose flints, in which the roots of grass freely run, and produce strong succulent shoots, which fall down, and taking root at the joints, send forth other shoots, which in like manner drop and root again, so that the stalk is frequently eight or ten feet in length from the original root; and though the crop is exceedingly thick, it is perhaps not 18 inches in height.

But this grass, though very abundant in these two meadows, prevails in most of the meadows which lie below them on the same stream; and whenever the winters are productive of floods, the grass in all of them is abundant in quantity and succulent in quality, and the hay is exceedingly nutritive; but in a year when water is scarce, their produce is extremely small, and of a very bad quality.

On examining other meadows in different bournes of this district, we find the same grass uniformly to abound in those situated near the spring-heads, and which in some years have plenty of water, and in others none at all. The same remark on its variation in quality and quantity, according to the wetness or dryness of the winter, is equally just.

The most probable way of accounting for it is, that it is almost the only grass common to water-meads that will stand wet and dry; for though it flourishes most when under water, yet no dry weather will kill it.

Clauses in Acts of Enclosure. – It is customary, and absolutely necessary in the enclosure of common meadows, to give the Commissioners full power to direct, alter, and regulate the flooding of the several allotments to be sent out therein; and great improvements might be made, if new carriages and drains were allowed out of the public funds of such enclosures.

[pages 137-148]

SECT. II. – SHEEP.

THE sheep stock of this district is an object of the greatest importance. It may, indeed, be called the basis of Wiltshire Down husbandry.

The peculiar aptitude of the soil and climate to sheep, the singular use of sheep-folding on arable land naturally light and loose, the necessity of making sheep the carriers of dung in situations where the distance from home and the steepness of the hills almost preclude the possibility of carrying it by any other mode, and particularly the advantages that art has given the farmers of this district of getting early grass, by means of their numerous water-meadows, whereby they are enabled to breed lambs both for the supply of their stock, and for the market, are the principal reasons which have contributed to give to give to Wiltshire the high rank it bears among the sheep-breeding countries.

The following pages respecting the Wiltshire breed of sheep, are entered here nearly verbatim form the Original Report in 1794. At that time the observations applied pretty generally to the country at large; they attach now partially throughout the two districts, and are therefore preserved. Some information respecting the present state of the sheep stock in South Wilts, will be found at the conclusion of this Section.

The number of sheep kept in this district cannot be exactly ascertained; but from the best information that can be collected, it appears that the number of lambs bred yearly is at least 150,000, and that the whole summer stock of sheep, including lambs, is very little, if any, short of 500,000.

Notwithstanding the seeming immensity, it is a fact, that the sheep stock of South Wiltshire has been for many years gradually decreasing, and that it is now less by many thousands than it was fifty years ago. On the sand veins, particularly on the rich parts of them in Pewsey vale, the introduction of a better mode of husbandry by the abolition of fallows, and the raising green crops, has tended to decrease the summer sheep stock; but as this system enables the occupiers to winter sheep for the down farmers, and that in a much better way than they were heretofore wintered, it may be said to be rather beneficial than injurious to the district.

But on the down part of this district, where the sheep-fold is indispensably to the production of corn, a diminution of the sheep stock is a serious evil. That this diminution has really taken place, and to a great extent, is a fact; but as many of the farmers who see it, and feel the effects of it, are puzzled to account for it, the cause is not very obvious; perhaps, indeed, it may be produced by a combination of causes. These are two that strike every person very forcibly, who has observed the husbandry of the county for the last thirty years, 'the pride keeping fine sheep, and the range there has been of late years for ploughing up the sheep-downs.' The former, by flattering the vanity of a farmer, prevents him from seeing his real interest; and the latter, by putting a temporary supply of money in his pocket, makes it his interest to conceal the future consequences, particularly from his landlord.

Purposes for which Sheep are kept in this District.

The best clue to this enquiry, is an investigation of the purposes for which sheep are kept in this district. The first and principal of these is undoubtedly the dung of the sheep-fold, and the second is the wool. The improvement of the carcass was not heretofore thought a primary object, and perhaps is in some degree incompatible with the great object of this district, viz. the hardiness of the animal, necessary to enable it to get its food on a close fed pasture; to walk two or three miles for that food, and to carry its dung the same distance back to fold; and the breeding lambs was looked upon as a necessary consequence, rather than as a primary cause of keeping such flock. A supply of ewe lambs for the keeping up this stock was necessary. The wether lambs lived equally hard with the ewes during the summer, and were sold in the autumn for the wether stock of those that had no convenience of breeding; and such of the ewes as were thought too old to breed, were sold off for fatting. On this system, the carcass either of the ewe or lamb was very little attended to.

But the practice of the breeders in this district is now almost totally altered. The first and great object at this time is the improvement of the carcass both of the ewe and lamb, and particularly of the latter, and the attention is directed much more to the quality of the lambs they breed than to the quantity.

The pride of having fine lambs, and consequently of having the name of selling them for the highest prices, certainly tends to lesson the stock of breeding ewes, and to exclude old ewes from that stock; and as such stock will not live hard enough to keep the Downs close fed, farmers have been induced to break those downs up under an idea of improving their sheep feed.

A great portion of this kind of land (as we have explained) produces at first both corn and grasses in abundance; but being thin and loose in its staple, is soon exhausted with a reception of crops: the grasses sown soon wear out. The coarse natural grasses, particularly the 'black couch,' or 'couchy bent' (*agrostis stolonifera*), and that in a starved reduced state, take possession of and cover the land, and a young tender-mouthed flock of sheep will rather starve than feed on it.

This evil has grown so serious, that many farmers who have the misfortune to find their in this state, have been obliged to drop breeding entirely; and as they must have sheep to dung their land, they keep a flock of wether sheep, which they renew from time to time by buying of their breeding neighbours.

The necessity, therefore, of keeping that kind of sheep that is most proper for the soil and climate of the district, and most suitable to the uses to which they are to be applied in it, is sufficiently obvious; but the question, 'Which is the best kind of sheep for Wiltshire Downs?' although it has been long and warmly agitated, has not yet been resolved: experience must and will hereafter decide it. It is not for me to pretend to a decisive opinion on so important a question, while so many intelligent experienced farmers differ so materially upon it; but I will endeavour as impartially as I can, to give the reasons adduced by each party in support of their respective opinions.

The kind of sheep which is chiefly kept in South Wiltshire, is what has been long known in Smithfield market by the name of the Wiltshire horned sheep: their wool is moderately fine, and particularly useful, being the kind of which the second, or what is called the super broad cloth, from 12s. to 16s. a yard, is generally made. The fleeces of a flock of Wiltshire ewes usually weigh from two pounds to two pounds and an half each; seldom higher than three pounds. The value of the wool has been for a few years past from 15d. to 20d. per pound; of course, the average produce of each fleece, has been about 3s. 6d. The weight of the carcasses of the wethers, when fat, is usually from 65lbs. to 100lbs.

It has been said, that horned sheep were not originally the general stock of Wiltshire; but this is not the object of the present enquiry. It is certain that no man living remembers when they were not the general stock; and it is as certain, that till within these few years, they were thought to answer the particular purposes of this district better than any other kind.

But the objectors against the present sort of sheep say, that they are much altered from the original kind of Wiltshire horned sheep, by the introduction of new rams; and that instead of being mended by the cross, they are become, in many respects, much worse for the purposes for which they are kept: the sheep in general were, till lately, certainly smaller than they are now.

The alterations that have taken place have been principally by breeding them longer in their legs, higher and heavier in their fore quarters, perfectly white in their faces and legs; with Roman noses, full eyes, and large open nostrils; wide in their bosoms, and little or no wool on their bellies:-in fact, by making them a much larger handsomer animal.

The opponents of the present kind of sheep say, that those alterations have made them less hardy and worse nurses, and in particular, so very nice in their food that they will starve on the same kind of land on which the old sort of sheep lived well; and that they are subject to disorders (particularly to the disorder called the goggles) which were not known till this alteration of the stock took place; they also say, that this new kind of sheep being so much nicer in their food, and rejecting the feed of the Downs, on which the chief dependence for sheep food is, have suffered the herbage to grow gradually coarser; and that the farmers, in attempting to remedy this evil, by shortening their stock of sheep, have made it worse; it being a well-known fact, that the closer the Downs are fed, the more stock they will keep.

Under these ideas, many attempts have been lately made to introduce new kinds of sheep, and particularly the South Down sheep from Sussex.

As this sort may not be known to all who read this Survey, it may not be improper to say, that they are a short-legged low sheep, without horns, and generally with black faces and legs; low and light in their fore quarters, but very good in their back and hind quarters; small and light in their heads and necks, and offals in general; full of wool, and that wool commonly very fine. The weight of their fleeces is nearly as much as those of the Wiltshire sheep, but the value is 8d. to 1s. per pound more; the wool being applicable to the uses in which the coarser Spanish kinds are employed, that of making an inferior kind of superfine broad cloth. The carcasses of the wethers usually from 55 to 80lbs. each.

How far this sort will answer, time and experience must determine. Those who keep them say, that they live so much hardier, and feed so much closer, that they can keep

300 well on the same land that would only keep 200 Wiltshire sheep; that they are more docile, will feed more contentedly, and stay more quietly in the fold; they also say that they are able, by keeping this kind of stock, to breed more lambs; and that the ewes are such good nurses, the lambs will be of equal individual value with the Wiltshire lambs; that the wool, by the improved quality as well as by the increased quantity, will almost double the profit they have hitherto had from Wiltshire sheep; and that by the increased number they keep, they will be better able to dung their arable land: and they see no disadvantage in them, but that the old ewes, when sold off for fatting, will not yield so much individually as the Wiltshire ewes; but then they say, 'that they shall have three to sell instead of two; and that the wethers, when fatted, always sell for a halfpenny or near a penny per pound dearer in Smithfield than horned sheep.'

In point of proportional beauty, they certainly cannot be compared with a Wiltshire sheep: how far their merits may tend to bring them into general use, time must determine. But an experiment is now making in many parts of the county, in consequence of the benevolence and public spirit of His Majesty, in procuring rams from Spain, and distributing them by means of the Bath Society, of the Earl of Aylesbury, and the Marquis of Bath, among other flocks, to ascertain how far the breed of Wiltshire sheep may be restored to those properties which their opponents say they have lost.

The Spanish rams appear to have those properties, or perhaps approach near to what the old Dorsetshire sheep were, before that sort had undergone similar alterations with the flocks of Wiltshire. History tells us, that the present race of fine-woolled sheep in Spain were sent thither from the Cotswold Hills, in Gloucestershire; but this must be a mistake, or the stock of Cotswold is entirely changed. Their present breed is a large, long-woolled, polled kind of sheep; whereas the Spanish rams which have been imported by the King, are a small, short-woolled, horned sheep: in fact, they resemble the Dorsetshire sheep much in their general appearance , save only, that their horns are more open and thinner the Dorsetshire sheep now are, and are more like the sheep now bred on Mendip Hills, and which appear to have derived their origin from the old kind of Dorsetshire sheep. The Spanish sheep have the tuft of wool on their foreheads which is common in the Mendip kind; they are a small compact animal, and though much lower in their legs than the present Wiltshire sheep, seem active, and able to walk a long way to fold: they are lighter in their fore quarters and offals in general; wide and good in their hind quarters; well covered with wool on the bellies, and down to the hocks; and therefore (though coming from a hot country) appear hardy, and capable of bearing cold. They appear to carry a much greater weight of wool, in proportion to their size, than Wiltshire sheep; and although they have been some years in England, their wool has been pronounced, by many good judges, to be equal to the immediate growth of Spain.

Disorder called the Goggles. – This disorder, we must observe, has tended more than all other reasons combined, to bring the Wiltshire sheep into discredit.

It is not clearly known when this disorder first made its appearance in Wiltshire, nor is it certain that it is peculiar to this kind of sheep. The symptoms are, that the animal becomes loose in the back-bone, with shakings in his hind quarters, preceded by a continued dropping of the ears.

It was very little noticed in Wiltshire till about 25 years ago; and yet it is certain that a disease, which was undoubtedly the same disorder, though called by another name, was known in Lincolnshire about 60 years ago. By a memorial delivered to the House of Commons in 1755, by the breeders and feeders of sheep in the county of Lincoln, it is stated, 'that for ten years then past, a disorder, which they called the rickets, or shaking, had prevailed among their sheep; that it was communicated in the blood by the rams, and would frequently be in the blood twelve months or two years before it was perceivable; but that when once a sheep had this disorder, it never recovered.' The disorder called the 'rickets' is now prevalent in some parts of Cambridgeshire, with the symptoms above-mentioned.

I am informed that all sorts of sheep are subject to this disorder, though known by various names; and that containing the same breed, without introducing rams from other flocks (provincially, *breeding in and in*), will produce it.

The reason, perhaps, why this complaint has been lately known as the Wiltshire disorder, is, that most of the Wiltshire wethers are sold off when lambs, and are fattened before they are two years old; and the pushing them with high keep at so early age, will most assuredly discover the goggles, if they be in the blood.

Many thousands that have been sold, not only from Wilts, but also from Hants and Dorset, have been attacked with this disorder; the sellers have been obliged to stand to the loss, and the sort of sheep has been in consequence brought into discredit. It has been, however, for a long time on the decline; and if care be taken in selecting rams, it will probably soon wear out.

No fair conclusion can ever be made as to the relative merits of the different kinds of sheep, till the contending parties are agreed on the purposes for which such sheep are kept. Many who have argued very violently on the subject have yet to learn, that sheep *bred for fatting*, are *bred to stand still*; sheep for folding are bred to walk. The latter was the great object which the old Wiltshire farmers had in view; the former appears to be, in a great measure, the object of the breeders of the present day. Each party contends that their favourite breed is the most profitable, for the general purposes of Wiltshire Down husbandry.

Conclusion on Sheep Stock.

Since the publication of these facts and opinions relative to Wiltshire sheep, the question respecting the comparative merits of that breed and the South Down, has been brought pretty nearly to a decision. I do not say that it is absolutely determined, because there are yet left, candidates for the original stock of the county. Public opinion, however, seems to have given a decided preference to the South Down; as the number thereof now kept in this district (including the crosses), compared with the Wiltshire horned sheep; bears nearly an inverse ratio with the stock of the two kinds in 1794. The South Downs were introduced into Wiltshire in 1789, by Mr. Mighell, of Kennett, they were afterwards crossed with Wiltshire ewes, and other breeds; but of late years, the pure natives of Sussex have been generally adopted. Perhaps the numerous crosses that were made with South Down sheep, may be traced to the desire of retaining some of the blood of their own breed, rather than to any objection to the new sort introduced; and as the pride of stock had at that time brought a large animal into the common flocks, it could hardly be expected that so great a change in men's minds was to be immediately effected. it has now been proved that the smallness of the animal is one of its great recommendations, in a country where summer food is scarce, and winter food raised with difficulty. The excellence of the wool, which has been increasing in price up to 3s. 6d. per pound, has also tended to recommend South Down sheep to Wiltshire farmers; the fine wool being much sought after, whilst the coarse wools are scarcely saleable at any price. The breed of lambs has been so much increased by this introduction, that I am confidently assured, full one-third more are raised in the county than under the former stock; it is even presumed that at this moment Wiltshire ranks, in point of number of sheep, nearly as high as any breeding county in the kingdom. The crosses of Spanish sheep into various breeds of this kingdom, as alluded to in the foregoing pages, were not carried to any great extent by landholders in Wiltshire till very recently. Some experiments were made, and so far as related to the improvement of the wool, they were very flattering; but the state of that peninsula not allowing our manufacturers to depend on Spain for the stock of wool hitherto received, any speculative men in this district, as well as in other countries, are now breeding Spanish sheep, as stock for general farming purposes, from the flocks lately imported by His Majesty. The result of the doubts which, 16 years ago, were entertained and expressed respecting the South Downs, makes me cautious of publishing opinions on this new sort of breeding stock. It is certain, the value of the wool will pay for some extraordinary care during the winter months, and particularly at the time when the ewes are yeaning; but it is doubted whether the general habits of Wiltshire farmers will permit them to pay this superior attention. The South Downs, being hardy, able to bear travelling, and excellent nurses, are very likely to continue the favourite stock of the district.

Annex 3
Floated Water Meadows
Decline of a Perfect System

Author's Note. I wrote this some ten years after work on the initial research had been published in 1982, having in the intervening period been otherwise occupied. It is largely derivative and thus tends to repeat material that will be found elsewhere in this volume. However it has not previously been published, it can be absorbed as a single entity and seems worth including here. It introduced some, then, new material and focuses on the debate about the how and when of decline. Re-reading it after 14 years there is an implicitly valedictory sense; the time of chalkland floated water meadows is over. But 14 years on that is not so, as I have tried to demonstrate at the end of Chapter 1. Two insertions below show how predicted publications materialized. This paper was given at the Wiltshire Local History Forum Annual Conference, Devizes 5 October 1991.

My concern with the floated water meadows of the Wessex chalkland is as an industrial archaeologist, not a local historian. In 1982, as introduction to a work for the South Wilts Industrial Archaeological Society, I wrote:

> An extensive, highly visible but frequently overlooked aspect of industrial archaeology in South Wiltshire, as well as more widely in the South West, is provided by remains of floated water meadow systems . . . [and] . . . Floated water meadows were a significant feature of the agricultural revolution in the Wessex chalk area during the seventeenth century. As an irrigation system they remained in general use until well within living memory. The purpose of this monograph is to place record the physical aspects of a number of examples in the Salisbury area and to make possible a clearer understanding of their characteristics.

What I say about the context of such archaeology, the operation of water meadows and their economic significance comes from written, secondary sources often very far removed from the basic evidence. The received wisdom is that a specialist system of irrigation, developed as a major improvement to the sheep/corn regime of the Wessex chalkland in the seventeenth century, was sustained unaltered until a combination of the arrival of artificial fertilizers and the agricultural depression from 1870 caused its usefulness to end. There must be more that can be teased out in individuals studies of villages, farms and families.

This picture [not reproduced] is taken from the eastern side of the Avon Valley above Salisbury and shows part of the system, still worked, at Lower Woodford. For centuries the value of this type of country lay in the corn that could be grown on the valley slopes. This in turn depended heavily on sheep, notably the Wiltshire Horn. These had little wool or meat value and were grazed on the downs by day and 'folded' to manure the arable at night. 'Floating' the valley bottom meant constructing the irrigation system that you see characterized by the corrugated effect of the ridges, each with its water carrier along its length, and drains between. This was operated so that different parts of the system could be flooded or 'drowned' during the winter. The ground was enriched by silt and the young grass, protected from frost, provided sheep with the 'early bite'. Later in the year an enriched hay crop provided fodder for bigger flocks to be carried through the winter.

This second slide [not reproduced] is of the complete Lower Woodford system, created about 1665. This is a semi-diagrammatic plan; the main carriage, central from top to bottom and closing the loop in the river is not reality as straight as that. The main hatch is at Point 1, right at the top, where the river flow can be diverted into this system. Numbered points down the Main Carriage indicate the series of hatches used to control the flooding of particular sections. Between Points 4 and 5 there is the pattern you saw in the earlier picture, the carriages along the ridges fed directly from the main carriage and the drains between flowing directly back into the river. Further down, beyond Point 8 more complex patterns of feeder carriages leave both sides of the Main Carriage as the valley widens out below the village. Water flooding the west side, away from the river, is carried back to it by tail drains through culverts under the main Carriage.

These culverts are one illustration of the engineering solutions needed to cope with the problems created by the varying topography of every loop to been exploited on every river. These were expensive creations but the investment mean the improved land supported more sheep and thus increased corn production. What happened in the nineteenth century to bring all this into decline?

For creative period in the seventeenth and eighteenth centuries we have rather good sources, such as estate papers and the records of legal disputes, well trawled (certainly for Wiltshire, Dorset and Hampshire). For operating procedures we have early agricultural text books and reports. Thomas Davis' report for the Board of Agriculture *General View of the Agriculture of Wiltshire* (variously cited as 1794 and 1813) is a good and well quarried source for most agricultural topics at the beginning of the nineteenth century. Later, in 1845 E Little in *Farming in Wiltshire* tells us that there were 'many vexatious and expensive law suits concerning water meadows in Wiltshire'.

Many of these sources have been drawn together in accessible form by Professor Kerridge, Dr Bettey and most recently by GGS Bowie. Kerridge published his early research, much of it from Wiltshire sources in *WANHM* in 1952 and 1953 and the *Economic History Review* in 1954. It is all consolidated in his *The Agricultural Revolution* 1967 but much is more readily accessible in the *Wiltshire VCH* Volume 4.

Joe Bettey, well known to many of you, amongst his mass of publications about Wessex includes work on The development of water meadows in Dorset during the seventeenth century in *Agricultural History Review* in 1977. This and a 1973 contribution to Exeter University's *Sheep, enclosures and water meadows in Dorset in the sixteenth and seventeenth centuries* which no doubt inform his more accessible general works, in particular *Rural Life in Wessex* (1977) and, more recently, *Wessex from 1000* (1986) in Longman's Regional history of England series. He also contributed the Development of Agriculture section to the 1977 *A guide to the industrial archaeology of Wiltshire* although in my view the diagram illustrating the principle of how a floated water meadow works is wrong.

In these various sources there is frequent reference to the extent to which creating floated water meadows increased the value of the land. As research material works through into increasingly summarized popular works the increased value is expressed in multiples of rental value to the landowner – threefold, sixfold, etc; or as a measure of increased hay output compared to an 'ordinary' meadow or an unimproved water meadow. For example, Bruce Watkin in his excellent, commendably brief and long needed *A history of Wiltshire* (1989) generalizes that 'water meadows produced four times as much hay as ordinary meadows' citing Bettey, the VCH and Davis (in this case dating the last as 1811, thus adding to the 1794 and 1813 I have already quoted!)

I stress this 'added value' because it obviously tends to explain why the system eventually extended the length of every chalkland river. For example, from tiny headwaters of the Wiltshire/Hampshire Avon at Jones's Mill above Pewsey without a break except where it passes through settlements down to where it needed really quite massive engineering work below Salisbury, through the Longford Estate (Nancy Steel's subject this afternoon) to Downton and below.

But the added value can be exaggerated. Which brings us to the relatively recent paper by Bowie (Watermeadows in Wessex – a re-evaluation for the period 1640 – 1850 published in *Agricultural History Review* Vol 35 Part 2 1987). His paper sets out to assess some of the published work of Bettey, Kerrige and others in the light of 'evidence from primary documentary sources'. Those he cites are predominantly from Hampshire, which does neatly complement the Dorset and Wiltshire complexion of the other two.

Bowie paints a rather fuller picture than I have come across anywhere else of change and development over the whole span of his chosen period. He firmly rejects the more exaggerated claims about second and third hay crops and quotes figures which are 'sufficiently similar to suggest an average which is far less than Kerridge would have us believe'. His own, perhaps wisely unstated, average suggest an added value of no more than double the unimproved value. But statistically his sample of primary source locations (Wickham, Broughton, Meonstoke, Stoke Charity and Otterborne Mead near Winchester) is strongly skewed to the eastern end of the Wessex chalk. An interesting exercise would be to re-evaluate all the primary source locations quoted over the years by Bettey, Kerridge, Bowie and others against the same criteria.

On the decline during the nineteenth century I would like to contrast summaries from Bettey and Bowie. The former, in the Wiltshire Industrial Archaeology Guide observes:

With the vastly increased use of artificial fertilizers the old role of the sheep as a walking dung cart vanished and the number of sheep kept in the county dropped from 774000 in 1870 to 73000 in 1954 . . . water meadows have almost entirely gone out of use; improved strains of grasses, new fertilizers, the heavy labour costs involved in their upkeep, and above all the difficulty of using tractors and heavy machinery on the soft ground of the meadows without damaging the intricate network of channels and drains, have all been factors in their decline.

The date range for the sheep population and the inclusion of twentieth century machinery as a factor position 'decline' as a later rather than earlier phenomenon. Contrast Bowie, quoting Little in 1845:

the real value of water meadows is not as great now' as it had been in the early nineteenth century, when 'it was thought impossible at that time for the sheep farmer to breed lambs on such farms as were not fortunate enough to possess them, but since the introduction and extensive growth of Swedes, turnips and other artificial food, many farmers that have little or no grassland, have produced lambs equal, if not superior, to those occupying the best watermeadows.

And later, he quotes a legal dispute over fifty two acres at Compton Malm split between two tenants, both subject to an indenture of 1782 specifying a rota for winter, spring and summer watering and who had collaborated on improvements in 1805 and 1816. However in the late 1820s one had built a new carrier and drain which 'materially injured' the other's meadows. Apparently the offender was dead by 1834 when judgement was given against his heirs who 'quit the farm soon after'. That is an example of development, perhaps ill considered, still going on well into the century; an example of that 'coincidence of interests' (quoting Bowie again) of those involved in watermeadow construction and maintenance – landowner, tenant and farmer, and watermill owner – (which) helps explain why watermeadows played such a crucial part in the development of the farming economy of the chalk down lands of Wessex during the period 1640 to 1850

But he also quotes a Dorset source in 1854 suggesting that the growth of roots and 'artificial' grasses had rendered meads less necessary but 'not less acceptable' in sheep husbandry. He concludes that

It is probable the problems about co-operation with neighbours, water supply and water rights and maintenance problems only influenced the decline of watermeadows when viable alternatives to their produce became available. Decline was slow and irregular both in area and time but the first signs of it can be recognized in the 1840s.

I think that is a fair observation; 1840 seems to me to be a more realistic bench mark from which to start charting decline than 1870 which always seems to me wrongly to suggest a casual link with the start of the agriculture depression. In 1840 also, we are reaching the era of the Wiltshire eight course rotation and 'Victorian High Farming' and perhaps Michael Stratton, later this morning will be able to comment from that perspective.

I have indicated that primary source evidence about development is to be found. But, although the system obviously no longer exists, and generalized reasons for this can reasonably be adduced, hard evidence for the how and when of decline is hard to come by. People tend not to record when they just stop doing something. I suspect that formal records, estate papers and farm records are unlikely to be much help here. We are looking more for diaries and letters. There is scope here for the local researches of local historians

I know of two eighteenth centuries diaries that throw light on the creation and operation of water meadows. Jeffery Whitaker's, published by the Wiltshire Record Society (Reeves and Morrison 1989), has some brief entries about the rather different 'catchwork' system at Bratton. For example, on 24 February 1740/1, 'let down the bays at Stokemead' – 'bay' meaning in this context 'a dam across a stream or ditch'

Any of you who heard the Dorset historian, Jude James, give the recent Hatcher Memorial lecture during Salisbury Festival will know that the Dorset Record Society will be publishing his transcript of the 1758 diary of James Warne, a tenant farmer of the Wool and Bere Regis area who makes substantial reference to such matters as the building of hatches. *[published as* Farming in Dorset; diary of James Warne, 1758 . . . *etc., James and Bettey (eds), Dorset Record Society 13, 1993. One particular entry about the collapse of a weir is quoted in Chapter 5]*

But where are the comparable documents for the nineteenth century? I am transcribing the Peniston letter books for the Wiltshire Record Society. These are a business record of two Salisbury architects from 1823 to 1858 who both travelled extensively and were, in succession, county surveyor with responsibility for bridges. So far I am up to 1824, have learnt a lot more about the treadmill in Devizes Jail but nothing about water meadows. I am hopeful that in the 34 years yet to come there will be at least the odd, perhaps indirect reference. *[In the event 34 years were not achieved and the work was published as* The letters of John Peniston, Salisbury architect, catholic, and yeomanry officer 1823 – 1830, *Cowan (ed), Wiltshire Record Society 50, 1996. Indexed as 'farmland, meadows' there are references to meadow structures in five letters; and no doubt many more to be found in those of the 28 years yet unpublished]*

There are some published recollections. AG Street in *Round the year on the farm*, written in the nineteen thirties [published 1941], describes the Drowner's work in November and goes on: 'The cows left the water meadows at the end of October but they will expect to find some nice green there again at the end of March. That is the greatest advantage of irrigated water meadows . . . they shorten the period of expensive feeding.'

He farmed at Wilton. In his lifetime the corn/sheep regime had gone and sheep, compared with previous centuries, had virtually disappeared. But the drowner lived on, still cost effective in a different context. This may be a distinction of some significance. The systems, as originally developed, may have declined with increasing rapidity from 1840 but still had value, a century later, for the simple purposes of early grazing and good hay. It is the pace and detail of this long slow process that is poorly documented. Unless of course, from your local researches, you local historians know better.

In identifying the decline in this way, partly within living memory, and if documentary sources are so lacking, perhaps we can use oral history. In this Forum's latest newsletter the reviewer observes that this is particularly valuable when, 'used to balance the view of history often provided by the description of important events or the doings of 'great' people'

Here we do not have great people but there are certainly broad generalizations, hypotheses, about fertilizers, heavy machinery, labour costs and so on to explain a great change in the agricultural economy. There is plenty of scope to balance this by using oral history. Local historians can gather that specific local detail needed to explain why a system, the extensive archaeology of which alone tells us was once so obviously and importantly in place, is now obviously simply not there.

Annex 4
Water Meadows in Hampshire

The leaflet reproduced on the following pages has been issued by Hampshire County Council, and is included here with the Council's permission, for which the author and publisher express their gratitude.

Policies

for the conservation of water meadows'
heritage and character in Hampshire

water meadows in Hampshire

Hampshire
County Council

Aim

To recognise and respect the importance of Hampshire's water meadows in all decisions concerning land management, structural and land use change in order to promote their positive management and conservation.

Introduction

Water meadows are an important and characteristic element of the Hampshire landscape. A recent survey has shown that all the major river valleys of Hampshire had extensive water meadow systems. The county is important in the overall distribution of water meadows nationally, consequently their management is both a local and a national issue.

Policy 1

The character and integrity of the remaining water meadows, and their settings, should be conserved recognising their local distinctiveness.

Landscape

Water meadows are a significant component of the valley landscapes of Hampshire. They are characteristic of the historic land use and make a distinct contribution to the character and appearance of the landscape. Their distinct open pastoral character is a key component of the valley landscape, highly visible from the surrounding higher ground. They are often set out in cogent and discernible blocks.

Water meadows are historically, functionally and visually related to their wider landscape setting and its management. They sometimes form part of significant river valley estates and are an integral component of these designed landscapes often developed for exemplary agricultural practice and sporting use. They vary according to the geography, topography and history of their setting, and this contributes to the local distinctiveness of an area.

Their special character is susceptible to erosion and loss through inappropriate land use, subdivision and management, including change to arable, abandonment with uncontrolled vegetation growth, tree planting, development and mineral extraction. Traditional management as permanent pasture would provide a conservation model. Proposals for change, conservation, management and enhancement of Hampshire's river valleys and floodplains should have proper regard for the character, distinctiveness and importance of water meadows.

It is important that the critical role of water meadows to the character of Hampshire's distinctive river valley scene be recognised, and that their conservation and management should be a matter of local, regional and national importance.

Policy 2

All decisions involving change should be properly informed, by survey where necessary, and proper recording should precede all irreversible change.

Archaeology

The origins and purpose of water meadows determine the archaeological elements of which water meadows are comprised. The drains and carriers, and the patterns that they form, create the essential character, and are often a reflection of the topography and date of origin. The built structures, such as sluices, aqueducts and bridges, provide additional visual elements. The archaeological aspect relies largely on these built and visible elements. There are few buried components and little complex stratigraphy. The archaeological integrity of the water meadows is maintained largely by the retention of visible features.

Where it is proposed to alter, destroy, remove or restore these features it is important that the proposals benefit from a full and proper understanding of the archaeological implication of those changes. In many cases it may be appropriate to carry out a full and proper archaeological survey to inform the decision. This should influence the proposed changes, and where it is decided that those changes should be implemented, to provide a permanent record of the archaeological resource before any irreversible change.

Policy 3

The conservation and repair of the built elements should respect the original character of the structure, and should be based on expert advice.

Built Structures

Some of the built structures are integral to the operation of the water meadow, such as bridges, sluices and aqueducts. There may also be ancillary features, such as races or sheep dips. They should not be needlessly or thoughtlessly removed or altered. Whilst their conservation may imply maintenance, and management of the land or restoration of a water meadow system may necessitate the need for repair, the removal or replacement of structures should be avoided where possible. Re-cutting of systems may also expose structures fully or partially buried and conservation to avoid rapid deterioration may be necessary. Where it is necessary to replace or repair a built structure, it will usually be necessary to take specialist advice. The structure should be recorded in its current state prior to any changes, which should be the minimum necessary. Appropriate materials should be used, either original materials reused, or materials that are sympathetic to the original structure used. A guidance note should be prepared and advice on appropriate materials obtained.

Management Guidelines

The management and conservation of water meadows can be influenced in many ways.

Owners have the most important role to play, but will often rely on specialist data and advice and on the policy and strategies of others to inform their choices. They may look to exemplary owners, such as local authorities, to lead the way. Many of these owners are fundamentally influenced by the context of the agricultural industry.

The Environment Agency has a key role in both protection and advice. In particular identifying water meadow issues in Local Environment Agency Plans, ensuring that Local Environment Agency Plans properly recognise the importance and vulnerability of water meadows and the manner in which their conservation and management might be influenced by the Environment Agency.

The Department for Environment, Food and Rural Affairs is able to influence the management of water meadows through Environmentally Sensitive Areas as well as targeting within the Countryside Stewardship scheme in relation to supporting the conservation of water meadows.

English Heritage might utilise a wide range of mechanisms and advice notes to support the positive management of water meadows and it might in some cases consider the role of scheduling to achieve preservation. It might also consider listing some of the built elements.

Where water meadows are threatened by development, or by mineral extraction, local authorities have an important influence, both in the policies within the Development Plan and in the determination of planning applications. Policies related to the historic landscape and archaeological remains will lend weight to the considerations of individual applications. The inclusion of historic landscape character within landscape assessment and the importance of historic landscape components within landscape strategies will allow these to influence land management and land use change in a positive way.

contact:

County Planning Department, Ashburton Court, The Castle, Winchester, Hampshire, SO23 8UE.

Telephone: 01962 846802/4

e-mail: planenv@hants.gov.uk

www.hants.gov.uk/ environment

Bibliography

D&G: *see* Dartnell and Goddard, 1894

VCH: *Victoria History of the Counties of England: Wiltshire*

WANHM: *Wiltshire Archaeological & Natural History Magazine*

Arnold-Baker, C, 1996, *The companion to British history*

Atwood, G, 1963, 'A study of the Wiltshire water meadows', *WANHM* 58, 403-13

Bettey, J H, 1973, *Sheep, enclosures and water meadows in Dorset in the sixteenth and seventeenth centuries* (Exeter Papers in Economic History, 8)

Bettey, J H, 1977, *Rural life in Wessex*

Bettey, J H, 1977, 'The development of water meadows in Dorset during the seventeenth century', *Agricultural History Review*, 25, 37-43

Bettey, J H, 1978, 'Water meadows', in Corfield, M C (ed.), *A guide to the industrial archaeology of Wiltshire*, 54-7

Bettey, J H, 1986, *Wessex from AD 1000*

Bettey, J H, 1999, 'The development of water meadows in the southern counties', in Cook and Williamson (eds.), 179-95

Bettey, J H, 2005, *Wiltshire farming in the seventeenth century* (Wiltshire Record Society 57)

Blith, W, 1653, *The English improver improv'd, or the survey of husbandry surveyed*

Boswell, G, 1770, *A treatise on watering meadows*

Bowie, 1987, 'Water meadows in Wessex: a re-evaluation for the period 1640-1850', *Agricultural History Review*, ????

Buckler, P, 1968, 'In search of new pastures', *Country Life*, 6 June 1968

Chandler, J H, 1983, *Endless Street: a history of Salisbury and its people*

Chandler, J H, 1987, *Salisbury and its neighbours* (Salisbury Civic Society)

Chandler, J H, 1991, 'Accommodation and travel in pre-turnpike Wiltshire', *WANHM* 84, 83-95

Clark, M, 2004, *The conservation of water meadows structures* (Hampshire County Council)

Cobbett, W, 1830, *Rural rides*

Cole, A, and Gelling, M, 2000, *The landscape of place-names*

Cook, H, *et al*, 2003, 'The origins of water meadows in England', *Agricultural History Review* 51

Cook, H, *et al*, 2003 online, 'Hydraulic conditions, oxygenation, temperatures and sediment relationships of bedwork watermeadows', *Hydrological Processes* 17 (9), 1823-43 [online journal, Wiley Interscience]

Cook, H, and Williamson, T (eds.), 1999, *Water management in the English landscape*

Cook, H, and Williamson, T (eds.), 2005 [forthcoming] *Towards a new treatise on watering* . . . (Windgather Press) [see page 22 above]

Cowan, M C, 1982a, *Floated water meadows in the Salisbury area* (SWIAS Monograph)

Cowan, M C, 1982b, 'Mysterious meadows: some aspects of the floated water meadows at Great Wishford, Wiltshire', *Hatcher Review* 14, 179-87

Cowan, M C (ed.), 1996, *The letters of John Peniston, Salisbury architect, catholic, and yeomanry officer, 1823-1830* (Wiltshire Record Society 50)

Cross, D A E, 1970, 'The Salisbury Avon navigation', *WANHM* 65, 172-6

Cross, D A E, 2003, 'Salisbury as a seaport', *Sarum Chronicle* 3, 35-44

Daniels, Peter, 1988, *Salisbury: a second selection*

Dartnell, G E, and Goddard, E H, 1894, *A glossary of words used in the county of Wiltshire* (facsimile edition, Wiltshire Life Society, 1991)

Davis, Thomas, 1794, *General view of the agriculture of Wiltshire*; 2nd ed., 1813

Defoe, Daniel, 1724, *A tour through the whole island of Great Britain*

Delorme, Mary, 1985, *Curious Wiltshire*; revised ed., 2001

Elliott, A, undated, *Maiden Newton Water-Meadow* (Dorset County Council leaflet, post-1991)

English Heritage, 2005, *Listing is changing* (leaflet)

Fawcett, S, 1978, 'The statue in the market place', *Hatcher Review* 5, 16-26

Foster, J, 2003, 'The story of Rose Cottage', *Friends of Harnham Water Meadows Trust Newsletter*, 23

Fraser, A, and Stamp, J T, 1968, *Sheep husbandry and diseases*

Goodland, N L, 1970, 'Farming the water meadows', *Country Life*, 30 April 1970

Harvey, G, 1979, 'Water meadow management the modern way', *Farmers' Weekly*, 16 Nov 1979

Harvey, N, 1980, *The industrial archaeology of farming in England and Wales*

Hony, G B, 1926, 'Sheep farming in Wiltshire, with a short history of the Hampshire Down breed', *WANHM* 43, 449-64

Hudson, W H, 1910, *A shepherd's life*

James, J, and Bettey, J H (eds.), 1993, *Farming in Dorset: the diary of James Warne 1758* (Dorset Record Society, 13)

Kerridge, E, 1952, 'The note book of a Wiltshire farmer in the early seventeenth century', *WANHM* 54, 416-28

Kerridge, E, 1953, 'The floating of the Wiltshire watermeadows' *WANHM* 55, 105-18

Kerridge, E, 1954, 'The sheepfold in Wiltshire and the floating of the water meadows', *English Historical Review*, 6

McKinley, J I, 2003, 'A Wiltshire 'bog body'?: discussion of a fifth/sixth century AD burial in the Woodford Valley', *WANHM* 96, 7-18

Musty, J, 1968, 'Water-mills on the River Bourne, south Wiltshire . . .' *WANHM* 63, 46-53

Lane Poole, E H, 1976, *Damerham and Martin: a study in local history*

Little, E, 1845, *Farming in Wiltshire*

Naish, W, 1716, *The City of Salisbury with the adjacent Close, church and river accurately surveyed* (printed map; 2nd ed., 1751)

Opie, I and P, 1951, *The Oxford dictionary of nursery rhymes*

Pevsner, N, 1975, *Wiltshire*; 2nd ed, revised B Cherry (The Buildings of England)

Ponting, G, 2004, *Scenes from a Hampshire childhood* (Miller Dale Publications)

Ponting, K G, 1979, 'Sheep in Wiltshire', *Wiltshire Folklife* 2 (3)

Reeves, M, 1978, *Sheep bell and ploughshare*

Reeves, M, and Morrison, J (eds.), 1989, *The diaries of Jeffery Whitaker, schoolmaster of Bratton 1739-41* (Wiltshire Record Society 44)

RCHM, 1980, Royal Commission on Historical Monuments, *City of Salisbury*, vol. 1

Rogers, K H, and Chandler, J H (eds.), 1992, *Early trade directories of Wiltshire* (Wiltshire Record Society 47)

Sandell, R E (ed.), 1971, *Abstracts of Wiltshire inclosure awards and agreements* (Wiltshire Record Society 25)

Seymer, R, 1665, 'Report to the Georgical Committee of the Royal Society on the agriculture of the Dorset and Wiltshire chalklands' Royal Society MSS, Classified Papers 1660-1740, 10/3/10

Shortt, H, 1957, *City of Salisbury*

Smith, C S ('Peter Gurney'), 1985, *Shepherd lore: the last years of traditional shepherding in Wiltshire* (Wiltshire Folk Life Society)

Stearne, K, 2005, 'Management of water meadows: four hundred years of integrated agriculture', in Cook and Williamson (eds.), 2005

Steele, N, 1982, 'Sir Joseph Ashe, Bt, 1617-1686: an advocate of watermeadows in good husbandry', *Hatcher Review* 2 (13), 125-32

Steele, N, and Tatton Brown, T, undated, *The history of the Harnham water meadows* (Friends of the Harnham Water Meadows Trust, post 1989)

Stephen, L, 1885, *Life of Henry Fawcett*

Street, A G, 1932, *Strawberry Roan*

Street, A G, 1936, *The gentleman of the party*

Street, A G, 1941, *Round the year on the farm*

Thake and Taunton, Messrs, 1931, *Fisherton Mills estate sale prospectus*

Thwaites, J R N, undated, *The history of the Wiltshire Horn breeed of sheep* (Wiltshire Horn Sheep Society)

Vaughan, R, 1610, *The most approved and long experienced water workes*

Vince, J, 1970a, *Carts and wagons* (Shire)

Vince, J, 1970b, *Discovering watermills* (Shire)

WANHS Cuttings 27, p. 41: untitled cutting from *Western Gazette*, 13 May 1971

Watkin, B, 1989, *A history of Wiltshire*

Whitlock, R, 1948, *Peasant's heritage*

Whitlock, R, 1976, *The folklore of Wiltshire*

Willan, T S, 1937, 'Salisbury and the navigation of the Avon', *WANHM* 47, 592-4

Wykes, I, 2002, *Water meadows in Hampshire* (Hampshire County Council)

After this work had been prepared for printing two further published sources came to light, in an unpublished PhD thesis. I am grateful to Dr Kathy Stearne for drawing them to my attention.

Wrightson, J, and Newsham J C, 1921, *Agriculture theoretical and practical: a textbook of mixed farming for large and small farmers and for the agricultural student*. [Professor Wrightson was apparently, inter alia, 'Late President of the College of Agriculture, Downton', in *c.* 1880].

'Irrigation' in *Encyclopaedia Britannica*, 9th ed., 1880, vol. 13. [This entry contains (pp.362-70) possibly the most extensive and accurate published description of how to build and operate bedwork meadows]

Index